Foundations

An Introduction to Christian Practices

Dr. Phil Maynard

Foundations: An Introduction to Christian Practices

2nd Edition: Revised and Updated for the 2020s

ISBN: 978-1-950899-14-2

Published by:
Market Square Publishing, LLC
Knoxville, Tennessee USA

Scripture quotations taken from the following versions of the Holy Bible as noted:

Dedication

Sometimes a book about growing disciples emerges from a deep desire to make a difference and sometimes the catalyst for writing is to fill a gap in the resources available to support the growth of maturing disciples of Jesus. This manuscript comes from both.

My thanks to those who have influenced my journey in spiritual formation including Brother Paul (my spiritual director); the faculty at Duke Divinity School who helped me explore the roots of spiritual formation in the Wesleyan tradition; my friends in the Emmaus Community who have encouraged the development of so many disciples over the years; and the congregations I have had the privilege to serve and explore the faith with over the years.

A special thanks to Becky, a constant source of encouragement and support. She was also the first to read and share excitement about the practices explored.

My prayer is that many will discover a deeper, more vital relationship with Jesus through these practices. There is nothing more important in life.

Table of Contents

Welcome!

***Foundations* is designed** to provide some basic Christian practices upon which we can build the structures and designs of our lives as disciples of Jesus Christ. The sections contained in this workbook are in no way a comprehensive treatment of the practices. In fact, each of the themes covered has been the subject of many books by renowned spiritual thinkers. Each chapter, however, is designed to offer a solid overview and a good place to start.

These materials were designed to meet the needs of local congregations looking for a hands-on, practical approach to introducing participants to the foundational practices for beginning a journey of discipleship (or refreshing our map for a journey begun long ago).

Discipleship: It's more than education...it's transformation.

One of the most important distinctions needed to understand the daily practices of discipleship is that they should be reflected in our behaviors. It doesn't really matter how many years we sit in Sunday School classes, attend Bible Studies, or faithfully attend weekly worship events if these practices do not inform the choices we make and transform the way we live. If education were all that was needed to make mature disciples, we would be the most discipled people on earth. But statistics show that this is simply not true. Research indicates that there is shockingly little difference in real-world behaviors between those who call themselves disciples of Jesus Christ and those who are non-believers. We think of ourselves as different, but too often we are not. Authentic discipleship is about actions that are guided by Scripture and formed by our relationship with Jesus.

Behaviors reveal our true values. Those values reflect our deepening understanding of the character of Christ. The spiritual disciplines guide us into a more complete experience of life as Jesus lived it. As we develop maturity in the ways we live out our faith, we begin to think like Jesus. We take on the same heart as Jesus. This is what maturity as a disciple looks like.

Intentional Discipling

Intentionality must be at the core of this discipleship process. It is not enough to assume we will "get it" by attending worship, fellowship dinners, or an occasional service project or fellowship retreat. Certainly, traditional Christian Education and small groups can play a part, but intentional discipleship must include some form of accountable relationships. This has been true from the era of the early disciples, it was the inspiration for John Wesley's discipleship system, and it remains imperative for today's church. Accountable relationships are the catalysts for authentic discipleship.

Here is one way to visualize the outcomes of authentic discipleship:

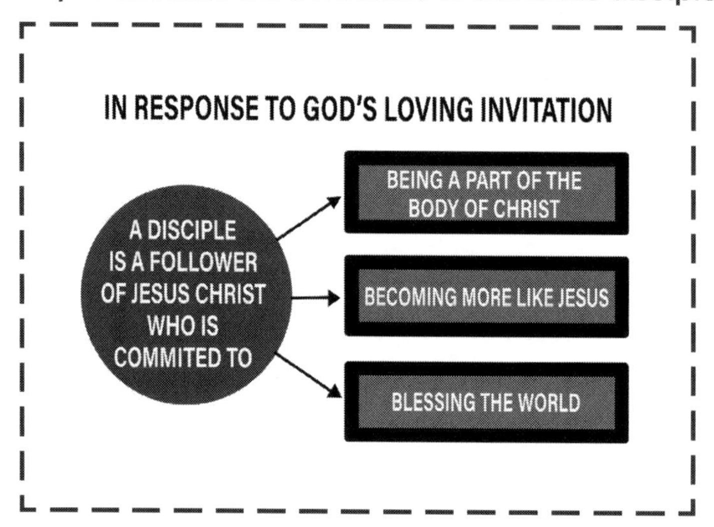

This visualization was crafted using familiar words from Jesus, found in Matthew 4:19 (RSV):

> *Follow me, and (being part of the body of Christ)*
>
> *I will make you (becoming more like Jesus)*
>
> *Fishers of men (blessing the world).*

It is important to note that there are no specifications for any of these three distinct stages as to how these directives will be lived out by unique individuals. Discipleship is a very personal journey. What works for one person will not necessarily work for another.

There is no "disciple-in-a-box"!

However, there are several dimensions of discipleship that relate to these three broad strokes identified in the definition.

Consider this graphic depiction of the six distinct dimensions of the discipleship journey.

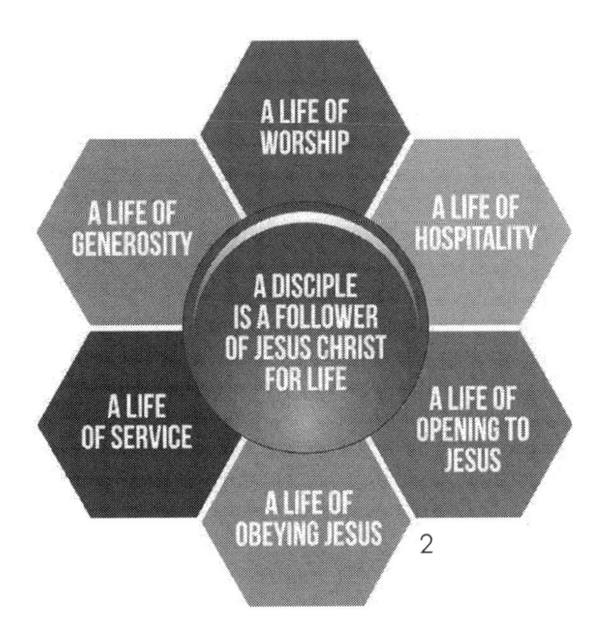

In **being part of the Body of Christ** locally, we live a life of worship and a life of hospitality.

> **A life of Worship** includes participation in corporate worship as well as personal worship (e.g. regular devotional time) and even a lifestyle of worship in which every action and circumstance becomes an opportunity to give glory to God.
>
> **A life of Hospitality** includes being part of the church community and welcoming new people to ministries. It also includes our interpersonal relationships with and loving acceptance of people who are outside the church and quite unlike us—even to the point of intentionally building relationships with persons beyond the church in order to embody Christ's love.

In **becoming more like Jesus**, we live a life opening to Jesus and increasingly obeying what Jesus has taught us. Together these reflect a commitment to intentional discipleship.

> **A life of Opening to Jesus** includes hearing sermons that teach the Scriptures, studying Scripture, and reading Scripture devotionally, but

it also includes engaging in those spiritual practices that develop our awareness of the presence of God. As followers gain maturity in this dimension, they take more and more responsibility for their own spiritual development and become less dependent upon the institution for their personal spiritual growth.

A life of Obeying Jesus involves becoming more like Jesus in our actions, attitudes, and responses to others. It begins with the acceptance of a relationship with Jesus and a commitment to grow as a disciple. We not only develop a Christian worldview in our daily living, but we also increasingly come to embody the example and teachings of Jesus. Jesus is Lord over all aspects of our life. Maturity in this dimension involves partnering with someone else who is just beginning their spiritual journey and helping them develop as a disciple of Jesus.

In **Blessing the World**, we live a life of service and a life of generosity.

A life of Service includes supporting the ministry of the local church with our time and energy and participating in service projects sponsored by the church, but it also includes a lifestyle investing the best of who we are in service to others as a matter of habit.

A life of Generosity certainly includes presenting our tithes and offerings as an act of worship, but it also includes creating a lifestyle with margins that allow us to respond to the needs of other people God places in our path on a daily basis.

This is Your Workbook

This workbook will become your guide and plan of action. This is not just for reading. It is a place for you to make notes on what you are learning, what you are experiencing, and what you plan to do in the future, based on your new insights. The more you utilize this workbook, the more it will become an important part of your personal Christian development.

Make a record of what you are learning and your goals for growing as a Christian, but also write down your hopes and fears related to those goals. Re-reading your hopes later can re-energize you in developing Christian practices. Writing out your fears and examining them can help you be more objective about them. Revisiting them later can help you see why you should not let your fears stand in the way of taking bold steps to come closer to Christ.

You may find that you are more comfortable working on one area (such as Bible study or private devotions) than you are on others. You may even find that focusing on one area gives you energy, while another drains you. This is natural. Building a strong foundation as a Christian, however, means developing in all of the practices included here. Perhaps you can use the areas in which you are stronger to fortify you for engaging the others. For example, a few moments of private prayer before you join a discussion or before inviting a friend to attend worship may give you the strength and focus to overcome your hesitations. You may want to paste a favorite prayer, Scripture verse, or poem into this workbook where you can see it when you need encouragement to keep going. Make this workbook your guide and personal transcript for the journey.

Truths about Adult Learning Taken into Account in Preparing this Material:

- We learn better when we know why it is important to know something.
- We like a variety of learning styles (e.g. visual, auditory, tactical).
- We remember more of what we are learning when we discover something, as opposed to being lectured about it.
- We like learning that engages both the right and left sides of the brain (the creative side and the logical side, which each have a role to play).
- We like to set our own goals for what we learn and do.
- We learn best within the context of one-to-one relationships that provide both insight and accountability.
- We like to try things on 'for size' and use what 'fits' best.

Building Christian Relationships as Disciples

"By this everyone will know that you are my disciples,
if you love one another."
John 13:35

A Relationship Inventory

Think about the many relationships in your life. They fall into many categories. Take a few minutes to categorize some of these relationships and think about how they help define you as a person, influence your choices, and determine your personal growth.

Here are some of my important **FAMILY** relationships (the people to whom you relate most deeply and most rely on for connection and support):

__________ __________ __________ __________

Here are some of my required **FAMILY** relationships (people to whom you are connected and obligated only because you are related):

__________ __________ __________ __________

Here are some of my **WORK ACQUAINTANCES** (people with whom you associate because of work but to whom you are not close):

__________ __________ __________ __________

Here are some of my **CASUAL FRIENDS** (people other than workmates with whom you may socialize or engage in hobbies, including neighbors):

__________ __________ __________ __________

Here are some of my **CLOSEST FRIENDS** (the people you turn to for support, or you enjoy spending time with the most):

____________ ____________ ____________ ____________ ____________

Here are some of my **CHURCH ACQUAINTANCES** (people you may frequently see because of church-related activities, but to whom you are not close in any way):

____________ ____________ ____________ ____________ ____________

Here are some of my **SPIRITUAL ACCOUNTABILITY PARTNERS** (people with whom you share your challenges as a growing disciple of Jesus Christ):

____________ ____________ ____________ ____________ ____________

While filling in those blank lines, you may have noted that some people fit more than one of these categories for you. You may have had trouble filling in all the lines for each category (or if you are very social, you may have needed more lines). You may have struggled to define the difference between friends, acquaintances, and accountability partners. Each level of relationship is useful to us, but the deeper levels are essential to our growth as human beings and our mental and spiritual health.

In the Gospel passage, John 13:35, Jesus declares the standard by which healthy relationships will be measured:

"By this everyone will now that you are my disciples, if you love one another."

This is a bold expression of love as a base for all relationships, but for our purposes, it is most importantly an agreed-upon reciprocity of active love (as demonstrated by Jesus' example) for those who would call themselves his followers.

The idea of authentic relationships is at the very heart of what it means to be a disciple.

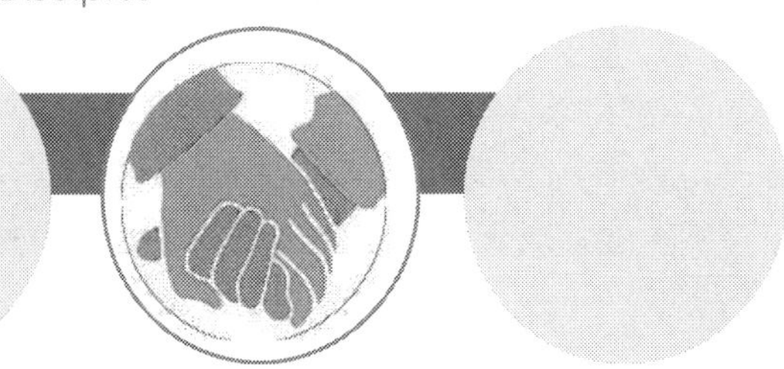

Love Your Neighbor as You Love Yourself

Of course, we often fall short of the standard that Jesus set for loving others (and for that matter, loving ourselves in the way that God loves us).

If you watch any "reality" television shows, read comment sections on the Internet, or even watch people in public, you have probably seen at least one minor disagreement escalate into a full-scale screaming match. Can you think of such an interaction that you have observed, whether on television, online, or in person?

What happened?

How did you feel watching it?

Opinion research consistently shows that Americans think people are getting ruder and meaner to each other. "Bullying" has been called an epidemic. And yet, between 75% and 80% of Americans (depending on the survey techniques) claim the title of Christian.

Even our personal relationships may seem increasingly fragile or potentially volatile. What are some examples of broken relationships that have troubled you...

- In the news?

- In your personal life?

Recent research in the area of Christian Discipleship has described an uncomfortable reality. The world does not see us (church participants, disciples) as reflecting the love of Jesus. In fact, statistics from the Fermi Project, a survey of 16-29 year olds, are pretty dismal:

- 87% perceive us as judgmental
- 85% perceive us as hypocritical
- 70% perceive us as insensitive
- 64% perceive us as not accepting of others' faiths

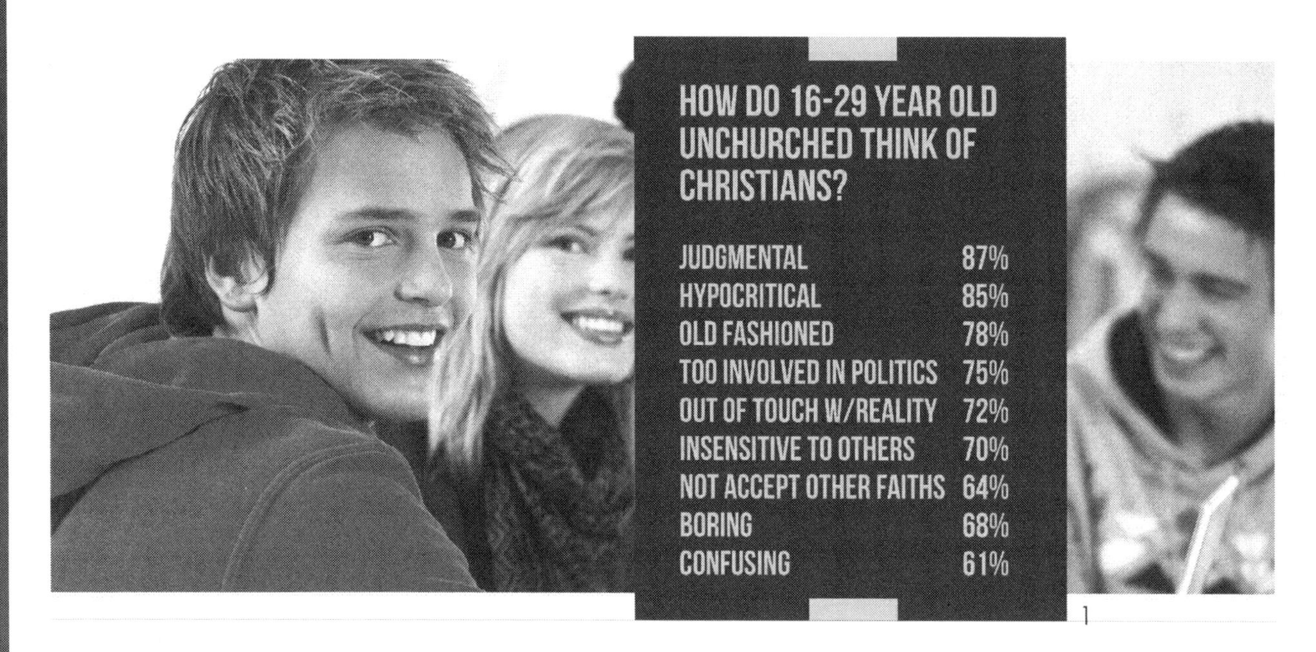

[1]

If the passage from the Gospel of John (13:35) is on target, "By this everyone will know that you are my disciples, if you love one another," it appears we have quite a way to go!

And yet, as we demonstrated earlier, authentic relationships are designed to be at the very heart of what it means to be a disciple.

Authentic Relationships

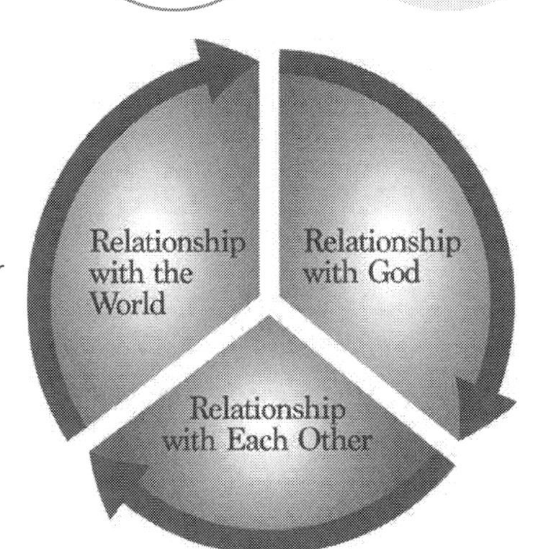

- We are called to be in relationship with God (Father, Son, and Holy Spirit).
- We are called to be in relationship with each other (modeling the relationship in which our Trinitarian God lives).
- We are called to be in relationship with those outside of the church.

As we grow in each dimension of our relationships, the other dimensions are impacted as well.

We could begin our discussion of building Christian relationships with our relationship with God or we could begin by focusing on people who are not in the church, but since we need to be able to work together as a group of disciples who are partners in trusting and safe relationships, it's a good starting point to begin with how we treat each other as Christians—within our own community.

Jesus' Prayer for Us

In John 17: 20-23, Jesus offers this prayer for believers…

> *My prayer is not for them alone. I pray also for those who will believe in me through their message, that all of them may be one, Father, just as you are in me and I am in you. May they also be in us so that the world may believe that you have sent me. I have given them the glory that you gave me, that they may be one as we are one—I in them and you in me—so that they may be brought to complete unity. Then the world will know that you sent me and have loved them even as you have loved me.*

Spend a few moments considering the implications of this prayer for understanding authentic relationships. There are several themes present in just these three verses. Try and identify at least two. **Write them down in the space below BEFORE reading on to the bottom of this page!**

The themes you found might include some of the following:

1. The "be one, just as you are in me and I am in you," reflecting on the unity of the Trinity.
2. The idea that as we grow in relationship with God ("be in us"), the world comes to believe in Jesus.
3. That we (believers) can in fact become one with each other as fully as the Trinity is one.
4. That it is Jesus' prayer that we experience unity as believers.
5. That our witness to the world depends on the kind of relationships in which we live.

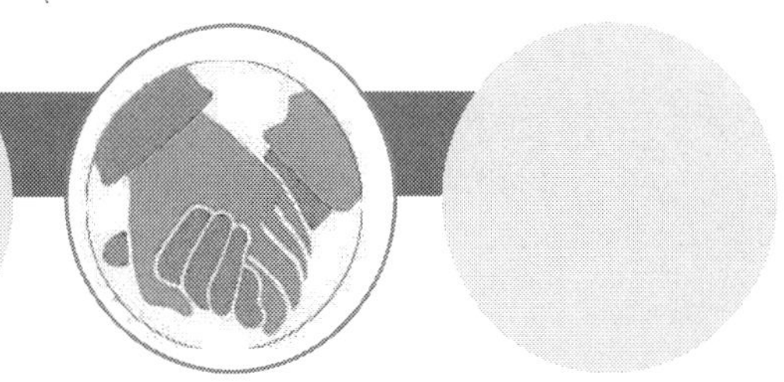

Christian Friendship

Noël Piper, a self-described introvert, was suffering from depression. She was in counseling, but no matter how hard she tried, she was getting more depressed, not less. One day her counselor asked her to name four or five "godly" women with whom she could be open. She named them, hoping he would suggest she talk to them and then drop the subject. Instead he told her to immediately contact them and ask them to come join the two of them at their next session.

She contacted each with brief pleas for help supplemented with many opportunities to say they were too busy. She really hoped they would say they could not participate, so that she might stay safely sheltered in her introversion. They surprised her, however, by saying that although they they felt inadequate to help her because of their own problems, they were honored to be asked and would be there.

Noël was glad there would be some women who, with time, she would not have to project an image of the woman she thought she should be, but she was anxious about the upcoming meeting.

> In my anxiety, though, I hadn't taken into account one essential thing: friendship goes both directions. These women weren't coming to examine me and work on fixing me. They were ready to give themselves and to receive from me and from each other.
>
> God showed Himself in the deep wisdom that sprang from their lives' stories of widowhood, life-threatening disease, physical disability, and victory over severe obesity. In their wider family groups were suicide, mental illness, prodigal children, and alienation... So from within their own history and daily experience, with tenderness, understanding, and empathy of experience they prayed for me, advised me, and gave me hope.
>
> To be fair, sometimes their words were not easy for me to hear. Often the phone calls, text messages, or emails were positive and encouraging. But sometimes a wise friend saw that I needed a rebuke, a reminder to call sin 'sin.' "Faithful are the wounds of a friend" (Proverbs 27:6, KJV).

Who can you trust enough to tell them when you've done something wrong?

Who can you trust to tell you the truth about yourself? Who can be honest with you when you are doing something wrong? Who can do these things without acting judgmental or gloating over your mistakes?

Who can you trust not to use your weaknesses against you in seeking praise or power for themselves?

If you have had such friends, describe them and your friendships.

Have you been a friend like that to someone else? Who were they? Describe your experiences with such friendships.

If you have had such a friendship, it was probably with someone much like yourself. Perhaps you liked the same movies, the same music, the same kinds of food. What did you have in common?

With whom could you be a friend like that, who might not have much in common with you? Someone you do not know much about except that they are also Christian? Someone in your church? Someone you might otherwise never even have met?

Christian Discipleship calls us to be in *trusting* and *trustworthy* relationships with others simply because we are all Christians. That kind of trust requires risk. We might get hurt. We might be embarrassed. We might fail them, or they might fail us. In fact, all of these are distinct possibilities.

But, there are many benefits of having authentic Christian relationships. They include:

- Synergy: power and energy that come from spiritual friendships.
- Challenge: motivation and influence to keep growing.
- Encouragement: bringing comfort, consolation, and counsel to one another.
- Accountability: objective counsel and fearless honesty.
- Support: people to come alongside and help us keep going.

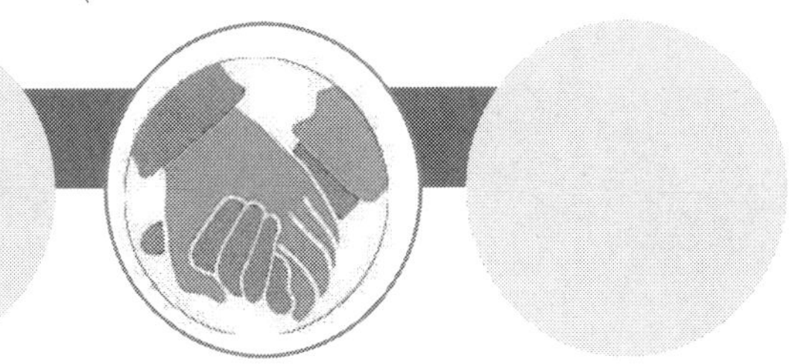

Characteristics of a Christian Relationship

Some practical considerations when it comes to living in authentic relationship with each other as disciples of Jesus include a focus on these two attitudes:

Forgiveness: Jesus said, "Blessed are the peacemakers" (Matthew 5:9). Paul said, "If it is possible, as far as it depends on you, live at peace with everyone" (Romans 12:18). How do you relate to people with whom you do not agree or who have hurt you? Jesus said that even sinners are nice to those who like and affirm them. "Love your enemies" (Matthew 5:44). "Bless those who curse you, pray for those who mistreat you" (Luke 6:28). Make peace with those who have hurt you. Our culture is strong on individual rights, on stressing what WE deserve and on what WE are entitled to in relationships. Jesus turned much of this upside down and said to those for whom he died while they were yet sinners, "Love each other as I have loved you" (John 15:12).

Acceptance: How do you accept and relate to those who are different from you? In nature, "birds of a feather flock together." But in the Kingdom of God, everyone is welcomed. This was hard for the early church to hear. The Holy Spirit expanded the early church's understanding of the inclusiveness of the Kingdom story by story, as if a bulldozer were knocking down every cultural barrier that kept people apart. Could sinners be welcomed? Could tax collectors and prostitutes? Could Greek-speaking Jews? Could Gentile God-fearers? Could Roman soldiers? Could godless Gentiles? Could those who had been worshiping foreign gods? The answer repeatedly was, "Yes!" God's welcome includes even them. And the early church struggled to welcome all of these different people into their table fellowship. Who might not feel welcomed by you into your small group or kneeling beside you taking communion? Jesus seemed to purposefully hang out with people who were not like him. What's more, they seemed to be drawn to his company. When you hang out with people not like you, are they drawn to you?

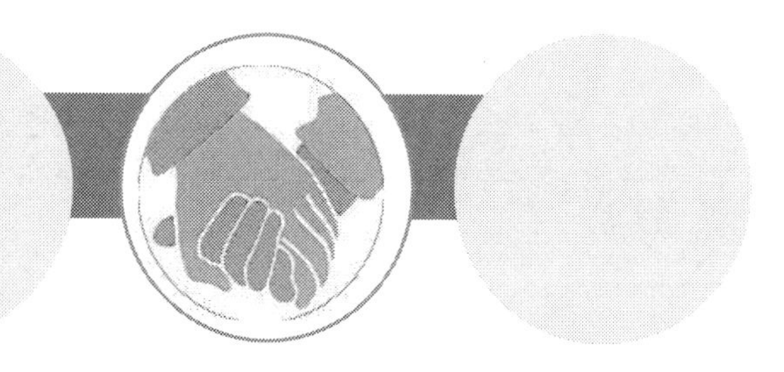

Covenant Relationships

Accountability is also at the heart of the Methodist Movement begun by John Wesley (see pages 26-27), as well as any transformational process of discipleship. Community and authentic relationships were supported through Class Meetings by a high level of accountability using a Covenant of Discipleship. Consider the following common elements of a covenant.

Covenant of Discipleship

- I will pray each day, privately, with my family and friends, and for my covenant members.
- I will read and study the Scriptures each day according to a plan.
- I will worship each Sunday unless prevented and receive the sacrament of Communion.
- I will heed the warnings of the Holy Spirit not to sin against God or my neighbor.
- I will heed the promptings of the Holy Spirit to serve God and my neighbor.
- I will prayerfully seek to care for my family and home and seek to help someone in need each day.
- I will prayerfully care for my body and for the world in which I live.
- I will prayerfully plan the stewardship of my resources.
- I will share in Christian fellowship each week where I will be accountable for my discipleship.

With whom do you have conversations about your discipleship journey? There are a variety of forms that authentic relationships can take within the church. Let's consider a few:

- <u>Small Discipleship Groups</u>: This is the most familiar form of relationship practiced in local congregations. While many different kinds of groups call themselves discipleship groups, we suggest that they need to include the following elements to

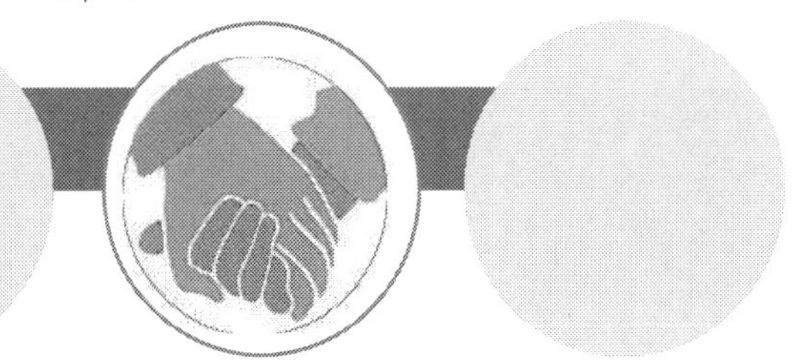

really be a discipleship group – sharing of community (prayer, fellowship, support, encouragement); becoming more like Jesus (time together that includes some component of transformed lives); and blessing the world/mission (some type of service together).

- Spiritual Friends: This is usually described as an informal relationship between two persons who commit to encourage, support, and hold each other accountable in the discipleship journey.

- Discipleship Coach: This is a more formal relationship with someone who has been trained in discipleship coaching. The coach assists the individual in identifying discipleship goals, building personal action plans, and providing a level of accountability.

- Spiritual Director: A Spiritual Director is trained to help individuals listen to the voice of God and respond to the guidance of the Holy Spirit. Spiritual Direction includes elements of seeking God, discernment, action steps, and accountability.

Being in Authentic Relationships Beyond Our Church

So far, we have been talking mostly about relationships with other Christians within your own church. While is it critical to our journey as disciples of Jesus that we develop and practice authentic relationships with one another, it is also essential, both for our journey toward maturity in Christ and for the building of the Kingdom of God, that we develop relationships with "unchurched" people so that they might be drawn to the love of Jesus through us.

Consider the contrast between two very familiar biblical characters: Jonah and Peter.

Read Jonah 1-2 and Acts 10.

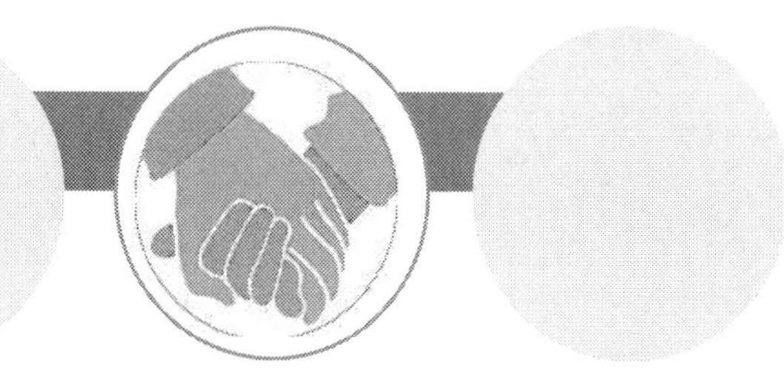

Which of these stories best reflects your attitude toward others?

Who would you find it most difficult to accept?

Recent research shows that in any given community, fewer than 50% of people are related to a community of faith. Most people who no longer attend church say they would be willing to try a church if a friend or acquaintance invited them. Yet relatively few church members invite others to their church.

The key to moving toward maturity in Christ is to start where you are! In the space below, name five individuals with whom you have a relationship but are not members of a local congregation (friends, neighbors, co-workers, parents of children on your youth soccer team, etc.).

What would it look like to intentionally 'be Jesus' to those persons for the next year? What difference might it make in their lives? What difference might it make for the Kingdom of God?

The journey of discipleship is demonstrated in outward behaviors that reflect an inner transformation. These behaviors are represented in steps toward maturity as identified below:

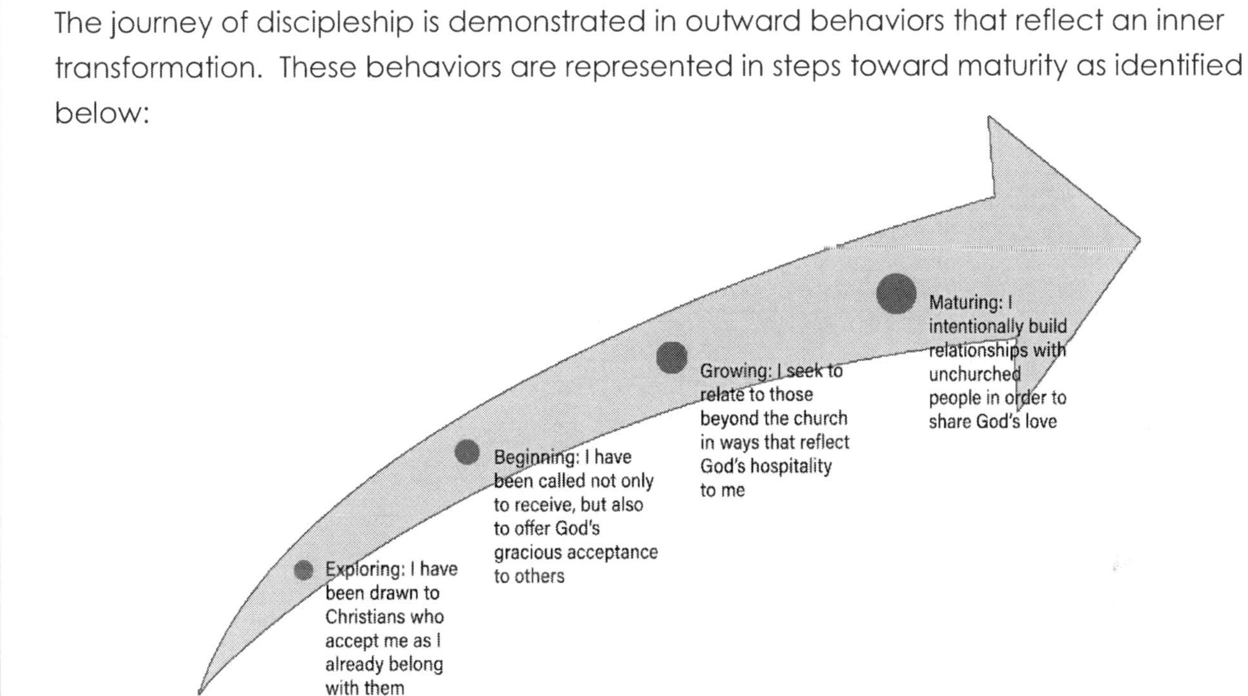

Where are you in this journey? What might your next step toward maturity be?

The practice (area) that I want to focus on developing is:

____

Someone who could support me in developing this is:

____

Resources that might be helpful:

____

1 Action Step:

When:

2 Action Step:

When:

The person who will partner with me:______________________________

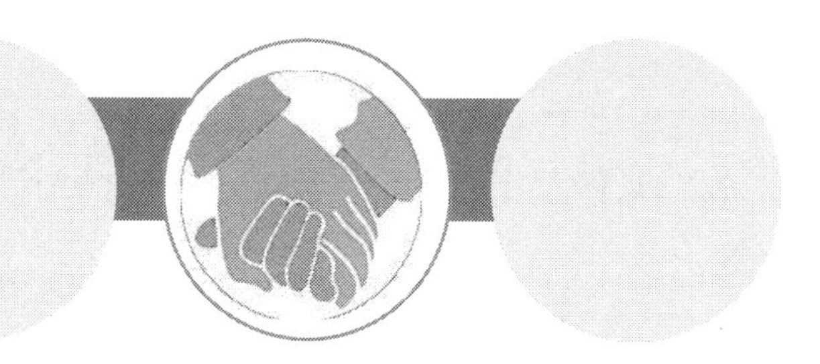

A Wesleyan View on Christian Relationships

John Wesley, the founder of the movement that would ultimately become Methodism, considered accountable Christian relationships to be a fundamental aspect of discipleship as Jesus intended. For Wesley, living holy lives required believers to share their struggles in intimate fellowship on a regular basis.

His development of small groups revolutionized 8th century England and provided a framework to help people grow in 'holiness of heart and life.' Small groups provided a context in which seekers could receive support, accountability, and encouragement.

This was especially important considering what he described as the temptations of the world and the disarray of the culture. Wesley's system of mutual accountability was divided into three formative aspects: **societies, classes,** and **bands**.

Societies primarily focused on educational channels through which the tenets of Methodism were presented. These tenets were taught in a large classroom setting, primarily through lecture, preaching, public reading, hymn singing, and 'exhorting.' In societies, people sat in rows, women and men separated, where they listened to a prepared lecture.

They were not given an opportunity to respond or give feedback.

John and Charles Wesley led the original societies until the movement expanded and lay assistants were delegated to oversee them in the absence of ordained clergy. The primary aim was to present scriptural truths and have those truths clearly understood.

Class Meetings were the most influential instructional unit in Methodism and probably Wesley's greatest contribution to spiritual growth. Class meetings get so much credit because they radically transformed England's working masses. The success centered on the instructional design of behavioral change.

Classes were intimate gatherings of 10 or 12 people who met weekly for personal supervision of their spiritual growth. Rules for the United Societies were the primary framework for the class meetings. Rules specified the basic process of 'inquiry' as to the subject matter of 'how their souls prospered.'

Class meetings were coeducational experiences that included women in leadership. Included in the sessions were those of diverse age, social standing, and spiritual readiness. Wesley wanted the classes to represent a cross section of Methodism. Also, the classes provided a place for believers to accept people from various social backgrounds. This helped break up the rigid class standards of 18th century England.

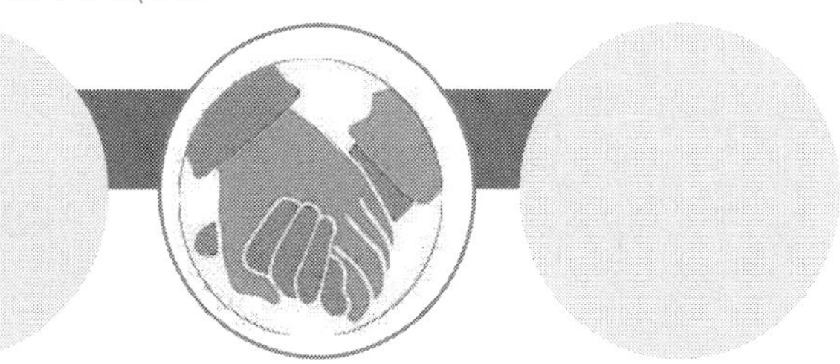

The leaders would share honestly about their failures, sins, temptations, or inner battles. They were the role models for others. Class meetings revolved around personal experience, not doctrine or biblical information. Perfect love was the goal of the class meetings.

Leaders were fellow strugglers who started the meeting, provided spiritual oversight or pastoral care to others, and were to carry the concerns of the class throughout the week. Leaders created an atmosphere of trust for all members to 'bear all things.'

Class meetings provided community and the development of class relationship and spiritual accountability for those who were struggling with habitual issues.

Bands facilitated affective redirection. Unlike the class meeting, the band was a homogenous grouping by gender, age, and marital status. Bands were voluntary cells of people who professed a clear Christian faith and who desired to grow in love, holiness, and purity of intention. Bands included ruthless honesty and frank openness. Members sought to improve their attitudes, emotions, feelings, intentions, and affections.

A central function of the band was what Wesley termed 'close conversation.' By this term he meant soul-searching examination, not so much of behavior and ideas, but of motive and heartfelt impressions.

Obviously, in modern times, it would be awkward and unwieldy to replicate Wesley's process completely, but we can transmit the important principles into our local congregations. Gathering in groups for spiritual accountability can help foster our faith and help us grow in Christlikeness. Being a faithful follower of Christ requires our investment in the journey of others.

Building My Relationship With God Through Prayer

Right at the depth of the human condition lies the longing for a presence, the silent desire for a communion. Let us never forget that this simple desire for God is already the beginning of faith.[1]

A Prayer Inventory

Think about the way(s) that you pray. Answer the following questions honestly. Feel free to check multiple answers for any given question, if applicable.

Excuses not to pray:
______ don't have the words
______ don't feel worthy
______ don't make time
______ feels unnatural
______ don't see results
______ not sure how
______ I don't know why

Frequency I usually pray:
______ many times a day
______ at least every day
______ frequently, but not every day
______ when I am so moved
______ when someone asks me to
______ when I face a crisis or have a need
______ only when: ______________________

When do I pray?
______ when I first wake up
______ fairly early in the morning
______ during the day
______ at night
______ just before going to bed
______ on Sundays
______ at no regular time

Where do I normally pray?
______ in a special place at home or at work
______ no particular place
______ in my church
______ in my car
______ outside in nature
______ wherever I am
______ other: ______________________

What has been the biggest influence on you in forming your attitudes and approach towards prayer:
______ what I have been taught by pastors and other "experts"
______ what I have observed in my friends and family and heard from others
______ what I have picked up from books that I have read
______ what I have learned in formal discipleship studies on the topic of prayer
______ what I have learned by trial and error

The reasons I pray are:
______ I find it useful
______ to converse with God
______ I enjoy praying
______ other people do it
______ God tells us to
______ I find it fulfilling
______ I don't know why

The results of my prayer are:
______ I feel close to God
______ God gives me direction
______ my spirit is renewed
______ they are answered
______ I am more sensitive to others
______ uncertain
______ mixed
______ confusing
______ other: ____________________

The things I pray about are:
______ my own needs
______ the needs of others
______ my gratitude to God
______ my worship (praise) of God
______ my sins
______ for guidance
______ the world
______ other: ____________________

How do I pray? (Feel free to check more than one).
______ formal prayers from memory
______ extemporaneous prayers
______ contemplation
______ conversational prayer with others
______ singing
______ meditation
______ "arrow" prayers for urgent needs
______ through worship in church
______ by listening

Attitude. I could best describe my feelings about prayer by the words:
______ necessary
______ satisfying
______ exciting
______ duty
______ joyous
______ difficult
______ confusing
______ mysterious
______ boring
______ adventure
______ ecstatic

I embrace:
______ praying in public when asked
______ sharing my needs with others
______ saying grace in public spaces
______ praying in the moment with someone
______ keeping a prayer journal
______ praying the Scriptures
______ kneeling to pray

Prayer Is a Conversation with God

At the heart of any real relationship is conversation, and this is especially true when it comes to our relationship with God. Consider, for a moment, when you were involved in a dating relationship. For some of you it may have been a few years ago! As you began the relationship, you started with some 'getting to know you' types of conversations, and even they focused on only the good stuff about you. As the relationship developed, the conversations became more personal, and you began to share what you liked and disliked, the quirks and foibles of your personality, as well as struggles and successes you were experiencing. As intimacy in the relationship began to grow, however, the conversations became more focused on the joy you found in one another and the needs each of you brought to the relationship. Eventually, the conversations turned to a delight in just being together.

Our relationship with God grows in much the same way, and the conversations we have with God—our prayers—follow much the same flow of developing intimacy.

This section is focused on how we can develop our relationship with God through prayer. While there will be some reflection on a couple of models of prayer, we want to emphasize that there is no right or wrong way to pray. What is important is not the how, but the what— or to use contemporary vernacular: Just do it!

*You can do **more** than pray, **after** you have prayed. But you can **not** do more than pray **until** you have prayed.*[2]

HOW Do I Start?

Start where you are. Spend as much or as little time as you need. There is no single right way to pray—let go of other people's expectations of what the "perfect prayer life" will be for you and find an approach that fits your lifestyle and prayer preferences. Speak your heart and listen for the heart of God.

Whether we think of or speak to God, whether we act or suffer for him, all is prayer, when we have no other object than his love, and the desire of pleasing Him.

John Wesley

"Again, truly I tell you that, if two of you on earth agree about anything you ask for, it will be done for them by my Father in heaven. For where two or three gather in my name, there am I with them."
Matthew 18:19-20

One way to build a prayer life is to pray with others. Choose someone to pray with once a week. It doesn't have to be anything formal or planned, and you could even start by exchanging prayer requests via email or text if praying out loud feels too daunting. Get into the habit of sharing the stuff you are longing to see God do with someone else: Praying together is powerful.

Consider praying with the friends we talked about in the first chapter. If you enjoy participating in groups, you may wish to join a prayer group, or you may even be led to start one. If you know someone who is ill or having surgery or facing some other need, you might wish to pray with them. This act of prayer could be the most important thing you have to offer them. Your church may have a prayer circle that lifts up concerns from individuals going through a difficult time who want the prayers of others.

Pray without ceasing
I Thessalonians 5:17 (NASB)

If God wants us to pray without ceasing, it is because He wants to answer without ceasing.[3]

Expect Conversation. Prayer is a two-way exchange between God and us. He loves to hear us and He loves to respond. Hearing from God is not some weird, wacky thing reserved for 'prophets,' and it did not end when the Bible was finished; He still speaks to us today. Listen for His voice today—it could come through the words of a song, a Bible verse, or a poster you see at a bus stop. You might hear Him through the encouragement of a friend, or He may give you a picture or speak in a voice you can hear.

How close to God do you feel as you pray? ______________________________

How close to God would you like to feel as you pray? ______________________

WHEN Shall I Pray?

Be realistic: If you set out to pray for three hours a day, you're likely to quickly become discouraged. Set yourself a smaller target, like 2 to 5 minutes a day and then work upwards as needed as your prayer muscles grow stronger.

Build prayer into your normal routines: There is a time for set prayer times, but sometimes the most authentic conversations with God happen on the move. Try thinking about Him when you are walking to college or work. Speak to Him about your fears or frustrations while you are waiting in the dentist's office. Pray for His provision and guidance as you walk around the supermarket.

When would you like to pray? ______________________________

"In the morning, while it was still very dark, he got up and went out to a deserted place, and there he prayed...."
Mark 1:35 (NRSV)

WHERE Shall I Pray?

Wherever you want. You might set up a prayer corner in your home, or you might feel closer to God sitting in your backyard or at a local park. Prayer groups across the country meet in church chapels, spare offices, empty classrooms, members' living rooms, and restaurants. My favorite place to pray is at the beach, while my wife has a chapel area set up in an extra bedroom.

If you find you want to spend more time praying or you need a time of spiritual renewal, prayer retreats are good ways to spend any length of time from a few hours to a couple of weeks focusing on prayer. These can be informal or formal, alone or with a group. Local monasteries and retreat centers sometimes offer retreats to non-members.

Where would you like to pray? ______________________________

WHAT Shall I Pray?

There are many different kinds of prayer. Some are spontaneous prayers for immediate circumstances, such as thanking God for travelers' safe arrival. Others are more structured prayers we pray to build our relationship with God. You might like to write out a list of prayer concerns before you begin. Or, you may want to pray what comes into your heart or head as you pray.

If you want to see how popular the church is, attend Sunday morning worship. If you want to see how popular the pastor is, attend Sunday evening. If you want to see how popular God is, attend the prayer meeting.[4]

Be Specific. Sometimes we skirt around the edges of the outcomes we really want to see because we are afraid to ask, or we are afraid that it won't happen and we will look silly. Practice asking God to do specific things, like healing the illness of a friend of yours, helping a relative to find a job, or giving you some direction about a decision you have to make, remembering to pray for God's will to be done.

There are many published books of prayers, and still more prayers are available on the Internet. Many of them are organized by topics. Prayer calendars of 21 or 30 days, or for the whole year, can help you keep going when you are not sure what to pray. You can make your own calendar with family members' birthdays, scheduled surgeries, important business meetings, special days in your church's year, and so forth.

Remember to pray for others, not just yourself. If you aren't sure how, one way is to hold their picture, or put it where you can see it, and ask God's blessings on them. This is a good way to think about your friends and family, but you can also use it to pray for your pastor and your church and even for the poor and oppressed. Some days the newspaper seems to have nothing but stories that need to be lifted up in prayer.

Use the Bible. Praying Scripture sounds daunting, but it really is simple. Pick a Scripture verse and apply it to the situation you are praying about. For example, "God, your Word says that in all things You work for the good of those who love You. Please use this situation to bring healing and peace" (based on Romans 8:28).

Plead the Promises of God

Armin R. Gesswein

Early in the ministry, I had an experience which completely changed my understanding of prayer. What a transformation! I was called to start churches and had just discovered 'prayer meeting truth' in the Acts. So, I started a prayer meeting—the first one I ever attended.

In came an elderly Methodist one night. When he prayed, I detected something new. 'I have never heard praying like that,' I said to myself. It was not only fervency—I had plenty of that. Heaven and earth got together at once when he prayed. There was a strange immediacy about it. The prayer and the answer were not far apart—in fact, were moving along together. He had it 'in the bag!' so it seemed to me. The Holy Spirit was right there, in action, giving him the assurance of the answer even while he was praying! When I prayed, God was 'way out there,' somewhere in the distance, listening. The answer, too, was in the distance, in the bye and bye.

Eager to learn his secret, I went to see him one day. His name was Ambrose Whaley, and everyone called him 'Uncle Am.' He was a retired blacksmith—also a Methodist lay preacher. I soon came to the point: 'Uncle Am, I would love to pray with you.' At once he arose, led me outside across the driveway into a red barn, up a ladder, into a haymow! There, in some old hay, lay two big Bibles—one open. 'What is this?' I thought. I prayed first, as I recall it. Poured out my heart, needs, burdens, wishes, aspirations, ambitions to God. Then he prayed—and there was 'that difference' again. There, in that hay, on our knees, at the eyeball level, I said: 'Uncle Am, what is it?...You have some kind of secret in praying...Would you mind sharing it with me?' I was 24, he was 73 (he lived to be 93), and with an eagle-look in his eyes, he said: ***'Young man, learn to plead the promises of God!'*** [Gesswein saw that he had lacked both Uncle Am's faith and his knowledge of the Bible.]'Uncle Am would pray Scripture after Scripture, reminding Him of promise after promise, pleading these like a lawyer does his case—the Holy Spirit pouring in His assurance of being heard. This man knew the promises 'by the bushel.' Gesswein began to make the Bible his prayer book.

PROMISES PREDICT THE ANSWERS. They are the *molds* into which we pour our prayers. They foretell what to expect. They shape our praying. They motivate, direct, and determine our supplication.

PROMISES LIKE THESE: *'Call unto me, and I will answer thee, and shew thee great and mighty things, which thou knowest not'* (Jeremiah 33:3 King James Version); *'All things, whatsoever ye shall ask in prayer, believing, ye shall receive'* (Matthew 21:22 King James Version); *'If ye shall ask anything in my name, I will do it'* (John 14:14 King James Version). [5]

Do you have favorite Scriptures or songs you would like to pray? What are they?

____

Is there someone you would like to pray for? Who? ______________________

HOW Shall I Pray?

Start with who you are, not what kind of 'pray-er' you think you should be. God gave each of us unique personalities, and the way we connect with prayer most comfortably reflects these. If you like the outdoors, go on a prayer walk. If you find creativity helpful, make a prayer collage or write a letter to God. If you prefer silence and stillness, shut out all the distractions for a bit and listen to God.

You may find saying a short prayer as you begin and another as you finish helps you focus this time on your relationship with God. A good ending prayer is "Thy will be done!"

The ACTS Model for Getting Started with Prayer:

One of the simplest and most well-known models for a prayer time is the ACTS format:

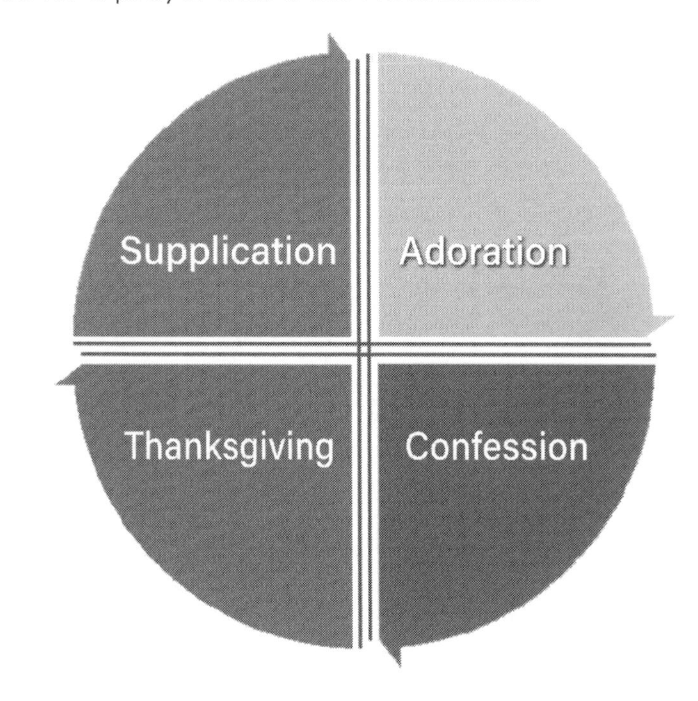

- **A –** **Adoration:** Proclaiming who God is and the attributes of His character.
- **C –** **Confession/Proclamation:** Personal cleansing, repentance, putting on of Christ's nature.
- **T –** **Thanksgiving:** Praise offering, remembering the works of the Lord, meditation.
- **S –** **Supplication:** Asking, intercession, and petitioning according to His will.

Adoration

Take time to adore the Lord and give Him the affection of your heart. Do *not* ask for anything. Focus on the attributes of God and declare who He is. Pray through the Scriptures. Psalms are especially a good place to find examples to give you language for your adoration.

Launching Pad Scriptures for ADORATION

Psalm 46:1 – "God is our refuge and strength, an ever-present help in trouble."

> **Praying the Verse**: You are the abundantly available God. You are always there when I need you.

Romans 8:38-39 – "[N]either death nor life, neither angels nor demons, neither the present nor the future, nor any powers...will be able to separate us from the love of God that is in Christ Jesus our Lord."

> **Praying the Verse**: You are the loving "for me" God. You are constantly by my side in every walk of life. Wherever I go, You are there waiting to show Yourself to me.

Confession

The ultimate struggle is that which we do against our own sinful nature. By lingering in the place of repentance, we advance against the kingdom of darkness. In this step, rid yourself of your sinful nature and take on the nature of Christ.

TIP: When you repent of a specific area, ask the Lord to clothe you in the opposite. Ask for joy instead of depression, humility instead of pride, pure love in the place of lust.

Launching Pad Scriptures for CONFESSION

Galatians 2:20 – "I have been crucified with Christ, and I no longer live, but Christ lives in me. The life which I now live in the body, I live by faith in the Son of God, who loved me and gave Himself for me."

> **Praying the Verse:** Jesus, I deny my sinful nature and ask that you would live in me. Let my life be a living example of You, teach me to be an ambassador of Your Kingdom.

Romans 12:2 – "Do not conform to the pattern of this world, but be transformed by the renewing of your mind...."

> **Praying the Verse**: O God, renew my mind. Transform my desires to match that which you desire.

Philippians 3:8-9a – "I consider everything a loss because of the surpassing worth of knowing Christ Jesus my Lord, for whose sake I have lost all things. I consider them garbage, that I may gain Christ and be found in Him...."

> **Praying the Verse:** Father, I leave behind anything that stands in my way of loving You. Loving You is the joy of my life, and I desire You more than anything. You are the one thing I desire, O God.

Thanksgiving

Speak to the Lord of the times He showed His faithfulness, or journal in a notebook about the times you saw Him move. This is a time of reflection and meditation. Do not ask the Lord for anything yet, just thank Him for what He has already done and remember the work of the Lord in every area of life.

Journal: Thank God for the following:

1 – God's Promises for your life

2 – People, family, co-workers, and friends

3 – Circumstances, miracles, experiences, and adventures with God

Launching Pad Scriptures for THANKSGIVING

I Thessalonians 5:18 – "[G]ive thanks in all circumstances; for this is God's will for you in Christ Jesus."

Praying the Verse: O God, thank you for all the blessings you have poured out on me and on mine. I will praise you in all things.

Psalm 136:26 – "Give thanks to the God of heaven. His love endures forever."

Praying the Verse: Thank you, Lord, for your steadfast love. I will keep thankfulness in my heart always.

Supplication

Ask the Lord to give you the desires of HIS heart. Base each prayer request on Scripture. By praying the Word, we align our will with His and remind the Lord of His promises.

You might choose to use apostolic prayers or the prayers of Jesus to give you language for your prayers.

Launching Pad Scriptures for SUPPLICATION

Psalm 109:1 – "My God, whom I praise, do not remain silent...."

Praying the Verse: Lord God, I cast all my anxieties on you because you care for me (from I Peter 5:7).

Ephesians 4:13 – "[U]ntil we all reach unity in the faith and in the knowledge of the Son of God and become mature, attaining to the whole measure of the fullness of Christ."

Praying the Verse: Let me with confidence draw near to the throne of grace, that I may receive mercy and find grace to help in time of need (from Hebrews 4:16).

Prayer needs three organs of the head, an ear, a tongue, and an eye. First an ear to hear what God says, then a tongue to speak, then an eye to look out for the result.[6]

Using The Lord's Prayer as a Model for Praying:

When the disciples asked Jesus to teach them how to pray, he gave them a model of prayer that has become known, and is often recited in worship, as "The Lord's Prayer." Let's consider this as a model for prayer:

Our Father in heaven...
How do you sense the loving presence of the Father (whom Jesus called Abba – Daddy) in your life today? What do you long for?

Hallowed be your name...
How might God's name be lifted up, made holy, in your life?

Your kingdom come...
Where in your life is there a need for God's reign?

Your will be done...
What guidance are you seeking from God?

On earth as it is in heaven...
Where is the gap between heaven and earth that needs to be filled by the presence of God?

Give us today our daily bread...
What needs do you have that only God can provide?

And forgive us our debts...
What do you need to confess to God, that you might be forgiven?

As we also have forgiven our debtors...
Whom do you need to forgive?

And lead us not into temptation...
What temptations are you facing today?

But deliver us from evil...
Where do you need God's protection?

For yours is the kingdom and the power and the glory forever...
Praise God! (Matthew 6:9-13).

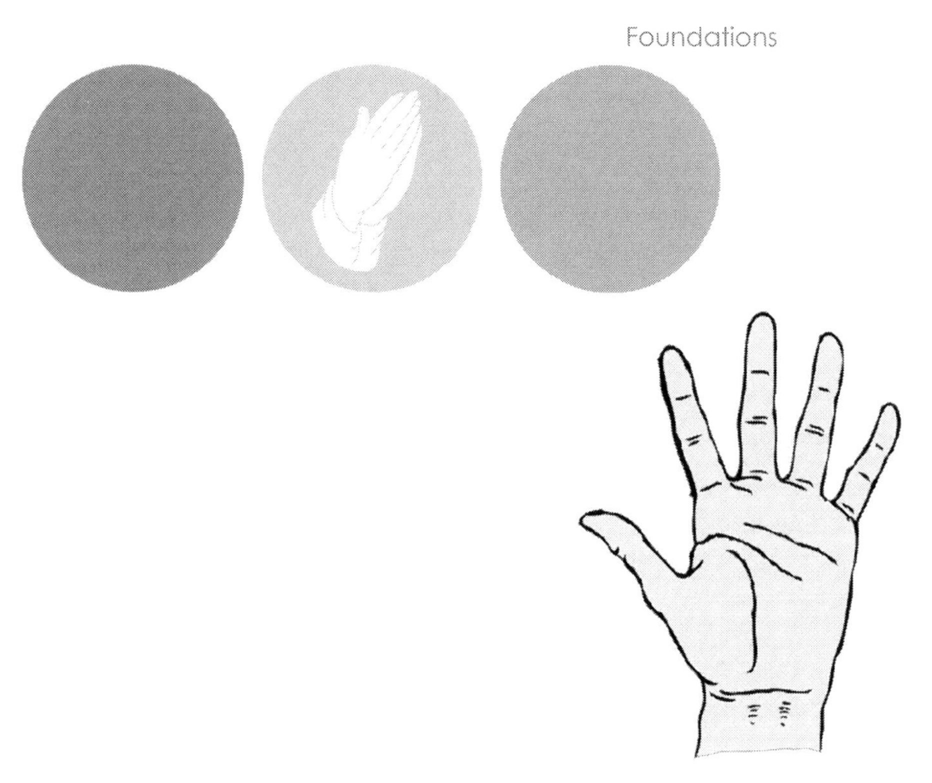

Using The Five Finger Prayer

Thumb: Pray for those closest to you (your family and friends).

Pointing finger: Pray for those who teach, instruct, and heal, that they will receive support and wisdom in pointing others in the right direction (teachers, ministers, doctors).

Middle/tallest finger: Pray for our leaders (the President, others in government leadership -- local, state, national, leaders in business and industry, administrators).

Ring/weakest finger: Pray for those who are sick, in trouble, underserved, and weak.

Pinky finger/the smallest finger of all: Pray for yourself last, which is where we should place ourselves in relation to God and others. By the time you have prayed for the other four groups, your own needs will be put into proper perspective and you will be able to pray for yourself more effectively.[7]

Try praying using one of these methods of prayer for a week. What was your experience with the method you tried?

____

How would you like to pray?____________________________________

What prayers would you like to pray?_______________________________

Prayer does not make us less involved in the world. On the contrary, nothing is more responsible than to pray. The more we make our own a prayer which is simple and humble, the more we are led to love and to express it with our life.[8]

What Do I Do AFTER I Pray?

Celebrate Answers. Sometimes we miss the stuff God does in response to our prayers. Sharing answers to prayer that you have seen can encourage others to pray and can be a reminder of what God has done in the past. Pick a psalm that praises God and read it through as a thank you to Him.

Mark the Journey. Journaling can help in building discipline into our prayer lives and showing us the bigger picture of where we've come in our prayer journey. Grab a notebook and write some of the stuff you are praying for at the moment, stick in some Bible verses or a card you were given that encouraged you. Write about the struggles and 'unanswered' prayers too, whatever you find helpful.

As you develop your prayer life, it can be helpful to end one session of prayer with preparation for the next. When and where will you pray again:

____

With whom will you pray? ______________________________

How will you pray? __________________________________

What will you pray? _________________________________

WHAT IF Prayer Doesn't Seem to Work?

Grapple with the silence. Sometimes we give up on prayer because things we have prayed for desperately just have not come about, or worse—the opposite has happened.

Sometimes we feel discouraged because we have prayed persistently for God to show us the right decision to make and have seemingly been met with silence. If this has happened to you, don't give up. Be honest with God and tell Him how you felt when His answer was far from what you asked; be angry at Him if necessary. Sometimes we don't understand His reasons; often this really hurts.

"Blessed is the one who perseveres under trial because, having stood the test that person will receive the crown of life that the Lord has promised to those who love him." James 1:12

The journey of discipleship is demonstrated in outward behaviors that reflect an inner transformation. In prayer, the movement is represented in steps toward maturity as identified below:

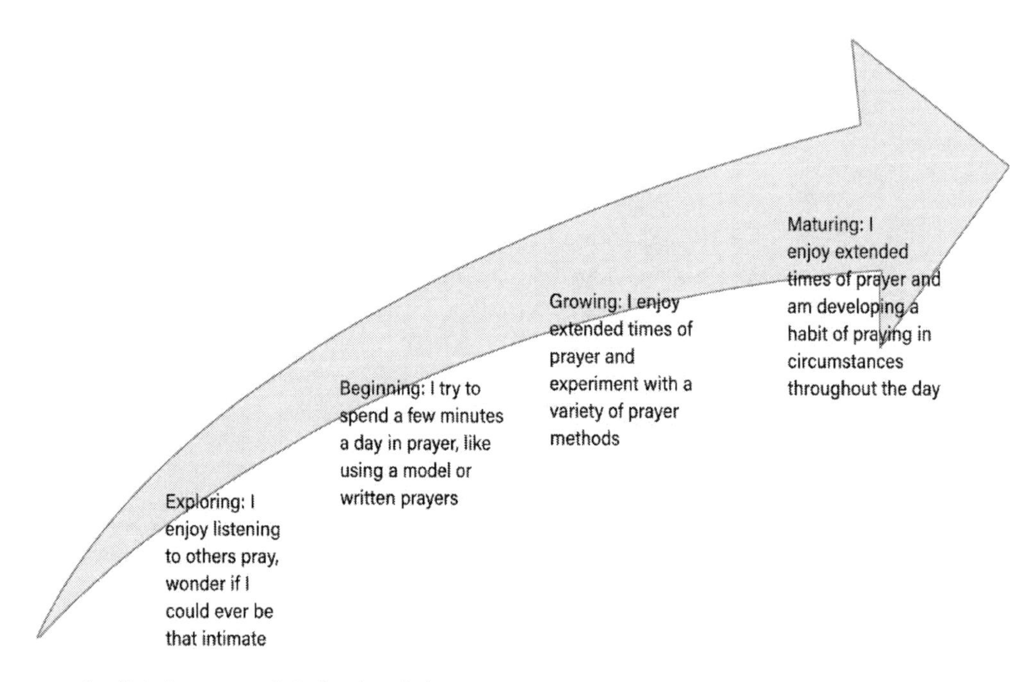

Where are you in this journey? What might your next step toward maturity be?

The practice (area) that I want to focus on developing is:

___

Someone who could support me in developing this is:

___

Resources that might be helpful:

___

1 Action Step:

When:

2 Action Step:

When:

The person who will partner with me:___

A Wesleyan Prayer Perspective

John Wesley was serious about spiritual growth, and he was correspondingly serious about his prayer life. Wesley believed that prayer was absolutely necessary "if we were to receive any gift from God," and he reportedly prayed four hours every morning, rising at 4:00 a.m. to do so. Additionally, he prayed in the moment as needs presented themselves, considering himself "instant in prayer" throughout his day. He considered prayer his intimate connection with God and his peace and power for daily challenges.

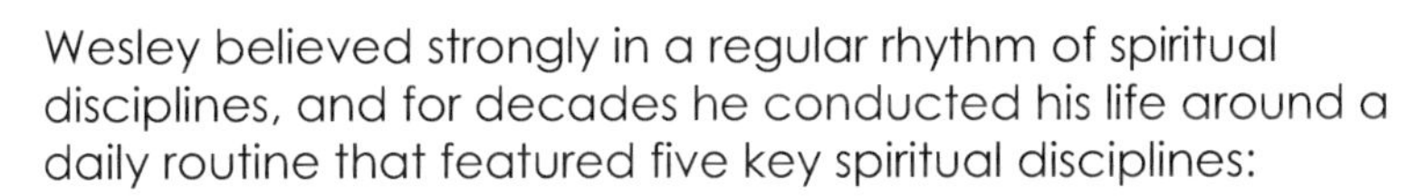

Wesley believed strongly in a regular rhythm of spiritual disciplines, and for decades he conducted his life around a daily routine that featured five key spiritual disciplines:

- <u>Prayer</u>: In addition to his morning prayers and the "in the moment" prayers of each day, he liked to begin each hour of each day with a brief prayer, and he made a point of anchoring all major decisions (personal and corporate) in a time of prayer.
- <u>Bible Study</u>: We'll consider this more in the next chapter, but Wesley considered himself a "man of the Book." He famously read through his Bible again and again while riding his horse from place to place. Prayer was used to contemplate those readings and those readings were frequently used as a script for prayer.
- <u>Journaling</u>: Wesley kept written track on a daily basis of prayer requests, answered prayer, general thanksgiving, blessings received, and other topics related to his prayer life.
- <u>Fasting</u>: Wesley had a regular routine of fasting, foregoing breakfast and lunch on most Wednesdays and Fridays and fasting combined with prayer when he faced difficult challenges or decisions.
- <u>Taking Communion:</u> The sacrament of Holy Communion, for Wesley, was an important means of grace, and made a point of receiving the Anglican communion once a week.

All of these spiritual disciplines were intertwined in their execution, and all were deeply connected to Wesley's prayer life. Every point of Christian action was, for him, birthed in prayer and anchored in prayer, each act of love towards his fellow men and women, and every decision in the spiritual journey that would lead to the fulfillment of the Methodist movement.

Wesley's Covenant Renewal Prayer

Among the most well-known prayers attributed to John Wesley is the so-called Covenant Renewal Prayer, a part of the Covenant Renewal worship service that Wesley adopted as a way for congregations to take an annual inventory of their own spiritual growth and fidelity beginning in 1755. It is a prayer of spiritual vulnerability, as we acknowledge God's power and offer ourselves without reservation in pursuit of God's will. Here is a version of the Covenant Renewal Prayer in language from the period in which it was written.

> I am no longer my own, but thine.
> Put me to what thou wilt, rank me with whom thou wilt.
> Put me to doing, put me to suffering.
> Let me be employed for thee or laid aside for thee,
> exalted for thee or brought low for thee.
> Let me be full, let me be empty.
> Let me have all things, let me have nothing.
> I freely and heartily yield all things to thy pleasure and disposal.
> And now, O glorious and blessed God, Father, Son and Holy Spirit,
> thou art mine, and I am thine.
> So be it.
> And the covenant which I have made on earth,
> let it be ratified in heaven.
> Amen.

Here is a version with more modern language, as paraphrased by Reverend Jeremy Smith:

> I am not my own self-made, self-reliant human being.
> In truth, O God, I am Yours.
> Make me into what You will.
> Make me a neighbor with those whom You will.
> Guide me on the easy path for You.
> Guide me on the rocky road for You.
> Whether I am to step up for You or step aside for You;
> Whether I am to be lifted high for You or brought low for You;
> Whether I become full or empty, with all things or with nothing;
> I give all that I have and all that I am for You.
> So be it.
> And may I always remember that you, O God, and I belong to each other.
> Amen.

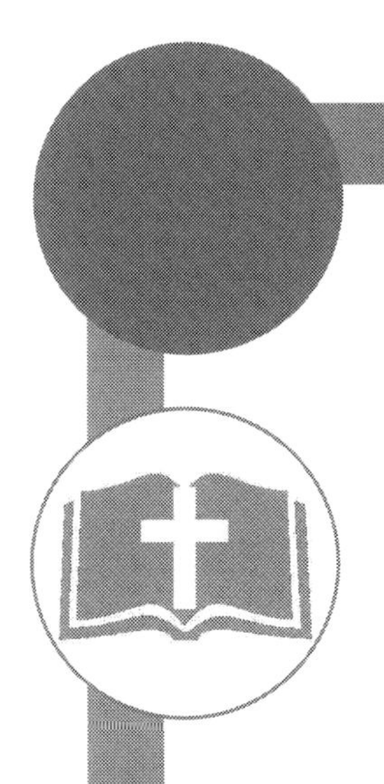

Building My Relationship with Christ Through the Word of God

All Scripture is God-breathed and is useful for teaching, rebuking, correcting and training in righteousness, so that the servant of God may be thoroughly equipped for every good work.

II Timothy 3:16-17

The Puzzle of Life

Take a jigsaw puzzle and empty it out upside-down on a table. DO NOT LOOK AT THE PICTURE ON THE BOX LID! Now try to put the puzzle together. Give yourself at least ten minutes to do this.

How did you feel while doing this exercise?

What would have helped you in completing the puzzle?

Most of life (much like this puzzle and many toys we purchase) comes with this note: "Some assembly required." Where do we turn to find the instructions for assembling our lives in the way God envisions?

In the beginning was the Word, and the Word was with God, and the Word was God. He was with God in the beginning. Through him all things were made; without him nothing was made that has been made. In him was life, and that life was the light of all mankind. The light shines in the darkness, and the darkness has not overcome it.

John 1:1-5

Knowing Jesus

What we know of Jesus as a person in history comes entirely from the Bible. Some people claim, like Paul (Acts 9), to have encountered Jesus through visions or ecstasies. After more than two thousand years of testimony from disciples who believe in and follow Jesus, however, we know that the only source about Jesus that is both reliable and available to everyone is the Bible. Fortunately, through all of its layering—telling and retelling songs, stories, aphorisms, legal codes, and so on—almost all of the New Testament and crucial portions of the Old Testament speak to us of the promised Messiah.

People come to the Bible for many reasons. Some come to hear the Word of God. Some come for the beauty of the language, the art of the literature. Some come for glimpses of an ancient world long gone in stone and structure, but with us in whispers and memory. Some come in search of evidence, to prove a point in an argument.

Some people come to the Bible because—taking all of the scholarly discoveries, all of the differences in translation and variations in texts, all of the curiosities and puzzlements in transmission around the world and through the centuries—they find Jesus available in and through the Bible in a way that invites them into and encourages them in a transformative relationship with God.

And beginning with Moses and all the Prophets, he explained to them what was said in all the Scriptures concerning himself.
Luke 24:27

The Big Picture of the Word of God

General Overview:

- There are 66 Books in the Old and New Testaments combined. Jesus Christ is the central figure.
- The Bible gives us a sweeping picture of God's dealings with humanity. It records what God has to say to humanity about who God is (character, thoughts, feelings, heart, actions), who we are (our sin and consequences, our potential), and how we are to live in relationship with God and each other.
- The common denominator in the Bible is relationships.
- The Bible is more of a 'who' or 'what' book, rather than a 'why' or 'how' book.

Old Testament:

- Comprised of 39 books.
- God's dealings with humanity from creation until 400 years before Christ.
- Includes: **Books of the Law**: Genesis, Exodus, Leviticus, Numbers, Deuteronomy (the beginning of all things and the beginnings of the people of God).
- **Books of History**: Joshua, Judges, Ruth, I Samuel, II Samuel, I Kings, II Kings, I Chronicles, II Chronicles, Ezra, Nehemiah, Esther (recording the rise and fall of Israel over a 1,000 year period).
- **Books of Poetry**: Job, Psalms, Proverbs, Ecclesiastes, Song of Solomon (written as poetry expressing teachings about God and life).
- **Books of Prophecy**: Isaiah, Jeremiah, Lamentations, Ezekiel, Daniel, Hosea, Joel, Amos, Obadiah, Jonah, Micah, Nahum, Habakkuk, Zephaniah, Haggai, Zechariah, Malachi (expressing the Word of God through people raised up in times of unbelief and rebellion).

New Testament:

- Comprised of 27 Books.
- God's dealings with humanity during and after Christ's time on earth.
- **Gospels:** Matthew, Mark, Luke, and John (record the earthly life and ministry of Jesus).
- **Acts:** This book records the movement of Christianity through the apostles' beginning of ministry following the resurrection of Christ.
- **Epistles:** Romans, I Corinthians, II Corinthians, Galatians, Ephesians, Philippians, Colossians, I Thessalonians, II Thessalonians, I Timothy, II Timothy, Titus, Philemon, Hebrews, James, I Peter, II Peter, I John, II John, III John, Jude (these books contain the inspired correspondence of the apostles and others chosen to communicate God's truth).
- **Revelation:** A book of hope and encouragement in the times of greatest trial for the emerging church, as well as a glimpse into God's final victory in the culmination of history.

Versions and Translations of the Bible:

Go to a church, library, bookstore, or website (such as BibleGateway.com), and you should be able to directly compare a few versions of the Bible. Choose a version of the Scriptures that works for you by reading a familiar passage in each of several versions (such as Psalm 23:4 below):

New International Version (easy to read/good translation)

"Even though I walk through the darkest valley, I will fear no evil, for you are with me; your rod and your staff, they comfort me."

New American Standard Version (closest to the Greek text)

"Even though I walk through the valley of the shadow of death, I fear no evil, for You are with me; Your rod and Your staff, they comfort me."

New Revised Standard Version (inclusive language)

"Even though I walk through the darkest valley, I fear no evil; for you are with me; your rod and your staff—they comfort me."

The Message (contemporary language paraphrase, very readable)

"Even when the way goes through Death Valley, I'm not afraid when you walk at my side. Your trusty shepherd's crook makes me feel secure."

King James Version: For over 200 years, there was only one English translation of the Holy Bible available: *The King James Version* (KJV). Written in the King's English (lots of thees and thous), it makes for very beautiful reading. Since that time, a large number of translations have become available that are easier to read and study, but there are many who still prefer to memorize (especially Psalms) in the language from the KJV.

Compare the following versions of Matthew 5:3-12

New International Version

Blessed are the poor in spirit, for theirs is the kingdom of heaven.
Blessed are those who mourn, for they will be comforted.
Blessed are the meek, for they will inherit the earth.
Blessed are those who hunger and thirst for righteousness, for they will be filled.
Blessed are the merciful, for they will be shown mercy.
Blessed are the pure in heart, for they will see God.
Blessed are the peacemakers, for they will be called children of God.
Blessed are those who are persecuted because of righteousness, for theirs is the kingdom of heaven.
Blessed are you when people insult you, persecute you and falsely say all kinds of evil against you because of me.
Rejoice and be glad, because great is your reward in heaven, for in the same way they persecuted the prophets who were before you.

New American Standard

Blessed are the poor in spirit, for theirs is the kingdom of heaven.
Blessed are those who mourn, for they shall be comforted.
Blessed are the gentle, for they shall inherit the earth.
Blessed are those who hunger and thirst for righteousness, for they shall be satisfied.
Blessed are the merciful, for they shall receive mercy.
Blessed are the pure in heart, for they shall see God.
Blessed are the peacemakers, for they shall be called sons of God.
Blessed are those who have been persecuted for the sake of righteousness, for theirs is the kingdom of heaven.
Blessed are you when people insult you and persecute you, and falsely say all kinds of evil against you because of Me.
Rejoice and be glad, for your reward in heaven is great; for in the same way they persecuted the prophets who were before you.

The Message

You're blessed when you're at the end of your rope. With less of you there is more of God and his rule. You're blessed when you feel you've lost what is most dear to you. Only then can you be embraced by the One most dear to you. You're blessed when you're content with just who you are - no more, no less. That's the moment you find yourselves proud owners of everything that can't be bought. You're blessed when you've worked up a good appetite for God. He's food and drink in the best meal you'll ever eat. You're blessed when you care. At the moment of being 'care-full,' you find yourselves cared for. You're blessed when you get your inside world - your mind and heart - put right. Then you can see God in the outside world. You're blessed when you can show people how to cooperate instead of compete or fight. That's when you discover who you really are, and your place in God's family. You're blessed when your commitment to God provokes persecution. The persecution drives you even deeper into God's kingdom. Not only that - count yourselves blessed every time people put you down or throw you out or speak lies about you to discredit me. What it means is that the truth is too close for comfort and they are uncomfortable. You can be glad when that happens - give a cheer, even! - for though they don't like it, *I* do! And all heaven applauds. And know that you are in good company. My prophets and witnesses have always gotten into this kind of trouble.

New Revised Standard Version

Blessed are the poor in spirit, for theirs is the kingdom of heaven.
Blessed are those who mourn, for they will be comforted.
Blessed are the meek, for they will inherit the earth.
Blessed are those who hunger and thirst for righteousness, for they will be filled.
Blessed are the merciful, for they will receive mercy.
Blessed are the pure in heart, for they will see God.
Blessed are the peacemakers, for they will be called children of God.
Blessed are those who are persecuted for righteousness' sake, for theirs is the kingdom of heaven.
Blessed are you when people revile you and persecute you and utter all kinds of evil against you falsely on my account.
Rejoice and be glad, for your reward is great in heaven, for in the same way they persecuted the prophets who were before you.

Practical tools and resources:

Everything written *about* the Bible, even interpretations of the Scriptures, comes from the perspective of the authors. You may want to read more than one resource to see different perspectives on any particular text.

Bible handbooks: Give a summary of every book and chapter in the Bible.

Bible dictionaries: Articles on people, places, things, events, and practices in the Bible.

Bible commentaries: Verse-by-verse studies of Scriptures with explanations.

Concordances: List every word found in the Bible and where it is found.

Bible Study Materials

There are a myriad of professionally written Bible studies available for those who want to grow closer to Christ. These include:

- Booklets for use by one person, for small groups, or for large groups.
- Daily devotionals that use Scripture, prayer, and reflections for daily inspiration.
- Guides that can lead you through the whole Bible in one year, two years, three years, or more.
- Booklets that explore one book of the Bible.
- Study guides for men's Bible study groups or for women's Bible study groups.
- Guides in different languages.
- Booklets for different ethnicities.
- Booklets on different topics in the Bible.
- Studies for seasons of the year, like Easter, Christmas, or Advent.
- Studies for people with disabilities or for their families.
- Guides for people struggling with addiction or other problems.
- Bible studies for people who are called to work with the poor or oppressed, with addicts, with the homeless.
- Studies for those who are called to evangelize with others.
- Studies for those who want to see their church grow and develop.
- Studies for leaders who want to lead by biblical models and principles.
- Studies based on gender, vocation, politics, art, and seasons of life.

I have known ninety-five of the world's great men in my time, and of these, eighty-seven were followers of the Bible. The Bible is stamped with a Specialty of Origin, and an immeasurable distance separates it from all competitors.[1]

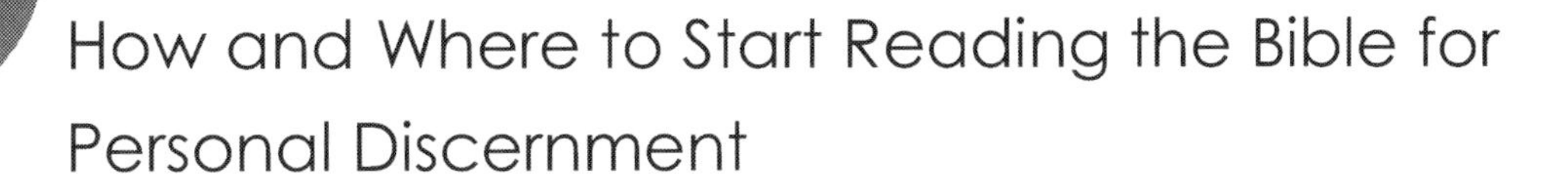

How and Where to Start Reading the Bible for Personal Discernment

The following are some suggestions for beginning the habit of listening and responding to what God says through the Scriptures. The purpose of reading the Bible is to know who God is so that we might grow in our relationship with God. Before you read, pray and ask God to reveal Himself to you, that you might fall more deeply in love with God each day.

While reading the suggested passages below, try the following:

1. Look for a verse that stands out to you or speaks to you personally.
2. Take a pen or highlighter and underline the verse.
3. Spend a few minutes meditating on how and why that verse spoke to you.
4. Using that verse, pray for yourself and others. For example, in James chapter one, your verse might be verse 5, which might be used in prayer like this:

   Praying for yourself: Give me your wisdom, God, that I might see life, myself, and people through your eyes. Thank you that you give wisdom generously.

   Praying for others: Please begin to reveal your truth and wisdom to:

   ______________________________________.

Read:	Favorite Verse:
James 1	______________________________
James 2	______________________________
James 3	______________________________
James 4	______________________________
James 5	______________________________

After James, begin reading the following books:

- **John** walks through the life of Jesus from a theological perspective.
- **Philippians** teaches a positive attitude during difficult circumstances.
- **Mark** shows the life of Jesus from another perspective.
- **Ephesians** relates all that we have been given in Christ and how to live.
- **Matthew** walks through the life of Jesus as written to the Jewish community.
- **Romans** gives the big picture of life and salvation from God's perspective.
- **Luke** presents the most easily read and understandable book on Jesus' life as written to the Gentile community.

Christ as Mediator and Advocate from Barbara Brown Taylor

God is greater than my imagination, wiser than my wisdom, more dazzling than the universe, as present as the air I breathe and utterly beyond my control.

That is, in short, what makes me a Christian. As the creature of a God like that, I need a mediator, an advocate, a flesh-and-blood handle on the inscrutable mystery that gives birth to everything that is. While Jesus is, in his own way, just as inscrutable, he is enough like me to convince me that relationship with God is not only possible, but deeply desired by God, who wants me to believe that love is the wide net spread beneath the most dangerous of my days....

For all the human handiwork it displays, the Bible remains a peculiarly holy book. I cannot think of any other text that has such authority over me, interpreting me faster than I can interpret it. It speaks to me not with the stuffy voice of some mummified sage but with the fresh, lively tones of someone who knows what happened to me an hour ago. Familiar passages accumulate meaning as I return to them again and again. They seem to grow during my absences from them; I am always finding something new in them that I never found before, something designed to meet me where I am at this particular moment in time.

That is, I believe, why we call the Bible God's "living" word. When I think about consulting a medical book thousands of years old for some insight into my health, or an equally ancient physics book for some help with cosmology, I understand what a strange and unparalleled claim the Bible has on me. Age does not diminish its power but increases it. When I recognize my life in its pages—when I am convinced that this story is *my* story—then I am lifted out of my own time and space and set free, liberated by the knowledge that my oddly shaped piece of life is not a fluke, but fits into a much larger and more reliable puzzle. In other words, I am not an orphan. I have a community, a history, a future, a God. The Bible is my birth certificate and my family tree, but it is more: it is the living vein that connects me to my maker, pumping me the stories I need to know about who we have been to one another from the beginning of time, and who we are now, and who we shall be when time is no more.[2]

The Journalistic Approach—Five Ws and an H

Journalists are often taught that when they report on anything they need to answer six basic questions about every story. These same basic questions can help us to understand what is going on in the stories told in the Bible. Pick a New Testament story you know well or one you do not know at all and try this.

Who? Can you identify who is in this story? How are they described? What is their relationship to each other?

When? When does this story take place? What length of time passes in the story? How do these events relate to other events chronologically?

Where? Where does this story take place? You may not be able to find it on a map, but how are the places described? (Bethlehem? Judea? A village? A house?) Are they related to other places? ("near the plot of ground Jacob had given to his son Joseph.") Are specific people related to a place? (Martha's house? Herod's palace?)

What? What happens in the story? What issues or topics are raised in the passage?

Why? Why does what happens happen? What motivates the people in the story to do what they do? Why does the author tell us the story?

There is another question that is not on this list, but journalists always try to answer it:

How? How do these events unfold? How do they relate to each other? How do they relate to other events in the Bible?

So What? What does this story tell you? How does this story help you understand something about your own life, the people you know, God, or Jesus?

"We must pay the most careful attention, therefore, to what we have heard, so that we do not drift away."
Hebrews 2:1

After you try this exercise with a story from the Bible, ask yourself: What did I discover that I had not noticed before?

Other Methods of Bible Study

Try each of the following methods with a passage you know well and with one you do not know at all. Can you begin to see which methods help you understand different kinds of Bible passages?

1. Theological Bible Study:
   What does the text say about God?
   What does the text say about humanity (us)?
   What does the text say about our relationship with God?

2. *Lectio Divina* – A spiritual reading of the Scriptures by stages:
   Silencio: Prayerful preparation
   Lectio: First reading of text, for hearing a word or passage that touches the heart
   Meditatio: Second reading of text, for "hearing" or "seeing" Christ in the text
   Oratio: Third and final reading of text, for experiencing what Christ is calling us to do or be
   Contemplatio: Prayerful yielding to God

3. A very practical tool made popular by Wayne Cordeiro is the S.O.A.P. method:

   S Scripture selection (read)
   O Observations (about the Scripture selection)
   A Application (how does this apply to my life?)
   P Prayer (focused on what God has revealed to you through the Word)[3]

The journey in discipleship is demonstrated by outward behaviors that reflect an inner level of maturity. In the diagram below, in reflection on Scripture, movement toward maturity might be demonstrated as:

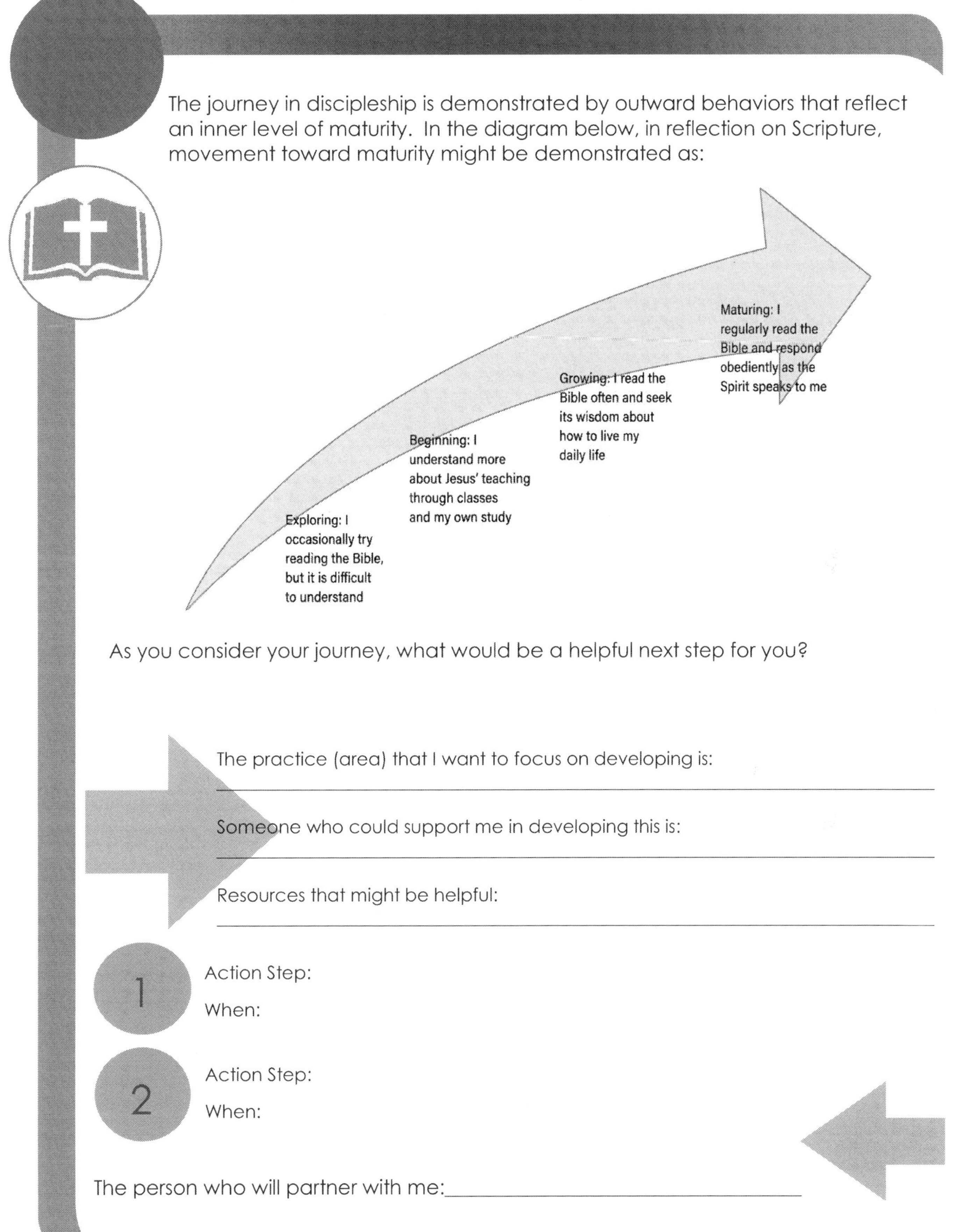

As you consider your journey, what would be a helpful next step for you?

The practice (area) that I want to focus on developing is:

____

Someone who could support me in developing this is:

____

Resources that might be helpful:

____

1 Action Step:

When:

2 Action Step:

When:

The person who will partner with me:______________________________

Wesley's Thoughts on Reading the Bible

Wesley called himself "homo unius libri," a man of one book (a phrase first attributed to Thomas Aquinas). In his Preface to the Old Testament in 1765, Wesley lays down some principles for reading the Bible:

- Set aside some time every morning and every evening to spend in the Word of God.

- If you have time, try to read a chapter from the Old Testament and a chapter from the New Testament. If you don't have that much time, read what you can. (Don't let the absence of the full allotment of time keep you from the benefit of reading even a smaller, more manageable portion.)

- Read with the focused aim of discerning God's will for your life, based on what you glean from your Bible reading. Make a firm resolution before you begin that as God's will is revealed as you read, you will commit yourself to following that revealed will as you understand it. Bible reading should lead to action.

- Read with the goal of growing your faith and being attuned to the ways in which theological themes of Original Sin, Justification by Faith, the New Birth, Inward Holiness, and Outward Holiness are connected and reinforce one another. (Each of these themes were, for Wesley, critical underpinnings of the theology which powered the Methodist movement.)

- Pray earnestly before and after reading the Scriptures, understanding the role that the Holy Spirit plays in revealing the power of God's Word.

- Make your Scripture reading part of a rigorous and forthright self-examination, noting where you are making progress in your spiritual walk and where you have fallen short and need more grace on the journey.

"If you desire to read the Scripture in such a manner as may most effectually answer this end, would it not be advisable, 1. To set apart a little time, if you can, every morning and evening for that purpose 2. At each time if you have leisure, to read a chapter out of the Old, and one out of the New Testament: if you cannot do this, to take a single chapter, or a part of one 3. To read this with a single eye, to know the whole will of God, and a fixt resolution to do it In order to know his will, you should, 4. Have a constant eye to the analogy of faith; the connexion and harmony there is between those grand, fundamental doctrines, Original Sin, Justification by Faith, the New Birth, Inward and Outward Holiness. 5. Serious and earnest prayer should be constantly used, before we consult the oracles of God, seeing 'Scripture can only be understood thro' the same Spirit whereby it was given.' Our reading should likewise be closed with prayer, that what we read may be written on our hearts. 6. It might also be of use, if while we read, we were frequently to pause, and examine ourselves by what we read, both with regard to our hearts, and lives. This would furnish us with matter of praise, where we found God had enabled us to conform to his blessed will, and matter of humiliation and prayer, where we were conscious of having fallen short. And whatever light you then receive, should be used to the uttermost, and that immediately. Let there be no delay. Whatever you resolve, begin to execute the first moment you can. So shall you find this word to be indeed the power of God unto present and eternal salvation."

–John Wesley

Wesley Believed That Scripture Reading and Study Were Essential to Spiritual Formation

John Wesley was focused on the believer's personal connection with Scripture as a path to its saving truths and formative power.

- Wesley believed we understand Scripture only with an invitation of the Holy Spirit to reveal its truths to us. He famously said that even "the devils" acknowledged the Scriptures, but they do not receive the truth and act upon it for their own growth and edification.

- Wesley believed that the Bible was best read "in conference" with others. This is why Bible reading was an unwavering part of every Society, Class, and Band meeting. It is important to surround ourselves with the wisdom of others who have been engaged in Scripture study for longer than we have (as well as life experience filtered through an application of the Scriptures).

- Wesley believed that human understanding has its limits. He said, "Although every man necessarily believes that every particular opinion which he holds is true (for to believe any opinion is not true, is the same thing as not to hold it); yet can no man be assured that all his own opinions, taken together, are true." Thus, Scriptural truth was important to set standards. This was also one of the reasons to be "in conference" with others, as it was important to learn from the experience and perspective of others --unfamiliar or unexpected insights from others can guard us against misunderstanding Scripture.

- Wesley had a particular interpretive tool in his Bible reading called "the Rule of Faith," in which he encouraged reading or interpreting any Scripture passage in the context of the themes of the Bible as a whole. If a passage was difficult, ambiguous, obscure, or seemingly contradictory, he believed that reading it through the lens of the grand narrative themes of Scripture was the proper approach and could help work through challenging passages.

- Meditation on Scripture was also an important tool for Wesley. In the formation of good habits and holy living, Wesley thought we are always at war with our less noble impulses. One of the best ways to build a rhythm of making holy, God-oriented choices, he thought, was to regularly meditate upon passages from the Bible.

Building a Life of Devotion Through Worship Experiences

When you think of worship, the first thing that probably comes to your mind is a gathering of like-minded believers who come together in a space set aside for that specific purpose to sing, pray, share liturgy, read Scripture, and hear a preacher. These worship gatherings are, of course, an important part of our faith walk together. This is called corporate worship. Answer the following questions to help think about the ways corporate worship experiences have formed your faith.

What is your earliest memory of a worship experience?

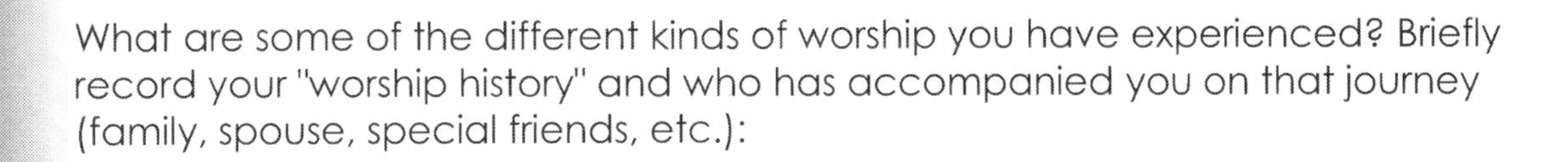

What are some of the different kinds of worship you have experienced? Briefly record your "worship history" and who has accompanied you on that journey (family, spouse, special friends, etc.):

Why do you think coming together to worship is important in our faith development?

In what ways is praying together as a group different than praying alone?

Is there any part of public worship that makes you feel uncomfortable?

What do you love most about participating in public worship?

Have you been part of an outdoor worship service? What was it like? In what ways was it different than the usual kind of worship in a sanctuary? Did this setting cause you to connect to God and others in a different way?

What are some of the most interesting places that you have worshiped?

How does art within a worship space influence your connection to God? (Stained glass, paintings, sculpture, banners, stage sets, etc.?)

Is your worship experience impacted significantly by factors such as lighting (sunlight vs. a darkened room, regular room lights vs. highly controlled theatrical lighting, colored lighting to reflect the mood, or the use of candlelight)?

Do you find it more worshipful to be in a very large room with a thousand people and a rockin' praise band or a handful of people and one leader with an acoustic guitar? Reflect on your feelings about group size, sound levels, music styles and the ways they impact the worship experience.

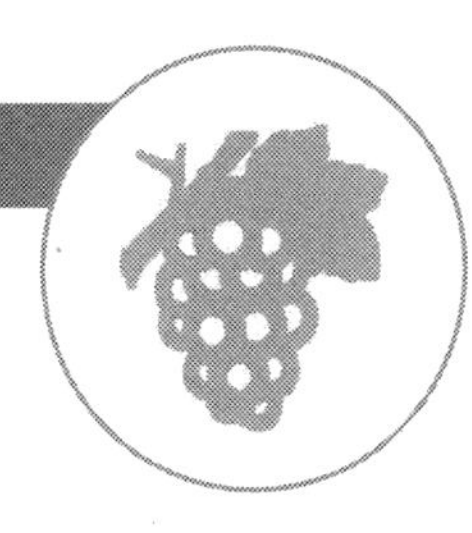

Worship as a Lifestyle Means
Personal Worship as Well as Public Worship

Corporate worship (worship together) is important, but as we mature as disciples we learn that an attitude of worship can be a part of our everyday routine.

Consider the following prayer/poem by Ted Loder in *Guerrillas of Grace*. Read it meditatively – slowly enough for the images to soak in:

...O God,
let something essential and joyful happen in me now,
something like the blooming of hope and faith,
like a grateful heart,
like a surge of awareness
of how precious each moment is,
that now, not next time,
now is the occasion
to take off my shoes,
to see every bush afire,
to lead and whirl with neighbor,
to gulp the air as sweet wine
until I've drunk enough
to dare to speak the tender word:
"Thank you";
"I love you";
"You're beautiful";
"Let's live forever beginning now";
and "I'm a fool for Christ's sake." [1]

What did this prayer communicate to you?

How did it make you feel?

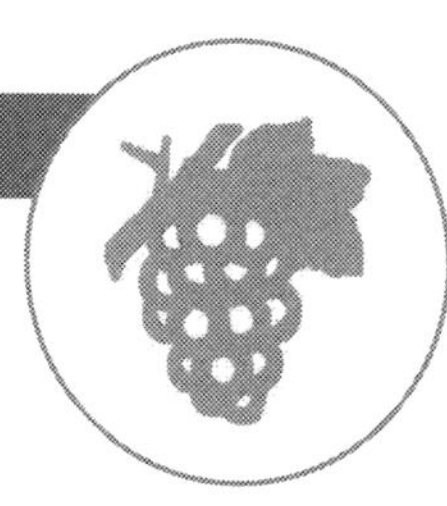

Developing a Life of Devotional Awareness

Jeff bought a mini-Cooper a couple of years ago. His son actually got him hooked up with a great deal on a slightly used model with all kinds of upgrades. After driving his new car for a few days, Jeff began to realize how many mini-Coopers there were around the area. He had never really noticed any of them before. But now that he was excited and focused on his new vehicle, it seemed they were just about everywhere!

We've all had situations like that.

In a sense, that is what cultivating a life of devotion is all about. A devotional time focuses our attention on experiencing God in the moment. And then, without even realizing how, we start becoming aware of God in all the moments of our lives and seek ways to honor God in those moments.

Worship and Relationships

Christianity has always had relationships at its core. We have explored some elements of these relationships in earlier chapters: Relationships between people, between people and God, and between people and Christ. Worship is a crucial place where those relationships happen. Some worship experiences are between an individual and God and some are among a group of Christians worshiping God together.

We tend to think of two polar opposites when we think of worship and relationships: either we mean worship in a large room full of other people, or we mean a time of personal worship/devotion. Keep in mind that worship can have great impact and offer new insights if done with just a few people. Such a worship setting offers expanded opportunities for interaction (such as praying together for specific requests or asking questions in response to a Scripture meditation, etc.).

"Let the message of Christ dwell among you richly as you teach and admonish one another with all wisdom through psalms, hymns, and songs from the Spirit, singing to God with gratitude in your hearts."
Colossians 3:16

Personal Devotional Time

There are many resources available to assist us in having a 'devotional life.' As a general rule, these resources profess the need and are designed for a time of devotion at either the beginning or end of each day. There is great benefit in setting aside such a time, but ANY time is better than NO time! The real value in those times is encouraging an attentiveness to God throughout all of life.

Spend a few minutes reviewing the following material related to having a set-aside devotional time. For each of the items suggested, feel free to write your personal witness indicating how this element of a devotional life is part of your routine.

What does a devotional time include?

The answer to this question is really personal! What works well for one person may not work at all for another.

Pick a time of day that works best for you: Some people prefer to start the day with a focus on God; others prefer to end the day that way; some like to do both.

Pick a place that works best for you: the image of a prayer closet (set aside space) is often suggested for a regular devotional time. As I mentioned earlier, my wife Becky has our extra bedroom set up as a chapel space. Personally I like to sit out on the deck and watch the sun come up or even better go for a walk on the beach where God and I can be alone together. The point is, find out what works for you.

Set aside some time that is just for paying attention to God: There are many who advocate setting aside an hour a day and others who get up early so they can spend multiple hours. For most of us 'normal' people, that may seem daunting. Start slowly!

Perhaps 5 or 10 minutes at a time would be a great starting point.

With Sighs Too Deep for Words

Likewise the Spirit helps us in our weakness; for we do not know how to pray as we ought, but that very Spirit intercedes with sighs too deep for words. And God, who searches the heart, knows what is the mind of the Spirit, because the Spirit intercedes for the saints according to the will of God.

Romans 8:26-27, NRSV

How to spend some time with God...

A great way to begin a devotional time is to offer praise to God. Some find that listening to or singing along with praise songs is helpful. Others begin by reading one of the Psalms of praise.

A devotional time usually includes a time of prayer. Consider one of the models for prayer suggested in this Foundations study. Prayer is the doorway into the spiritual realm; it anchors us firmly to God, and it 'works the earth of the heart,' to draw on the imagery of ancient monastics, as noted by Kathleen Norris in *The Cloister Walk*.[2]

Spending time in the Word (the Scriptures) is also a good part of a devotional time. I would like to point out that devotional reading of the Word is different from the study of the Scriptures. Study is designed to expand our understanding of the Scriptures.

Devotional reading is designed to expand our awareness of God in our midst. The SOAP model[3] is an example of devotional reading. So, too, are spiritual practices like reflective Bible study, meditation on Scripture, and praying the Scriptures.

The practice of meditation allows the words of Scripture to penetrate our hearts. Literally it means to "mutter" or to "mumble" and is the habit of people reflecting on Scripture by turning it over and over again in their minds and often speaking the words in a whisper over and over again. Psalm 1 highlights the value of meditation:

> Blessed is the one
> who does not walk in step with the wicked
> or stand in the way that sinners take
> or sit in the company of mockers,
> but whose delight is in the law of the LORD,
> and who meditates on his law day and night.
> That person is like a tree planted by streams of water,
> which yields its fruit in season
> and whose leaf does not wither—
> whatever they do prospers (verses 1-3).

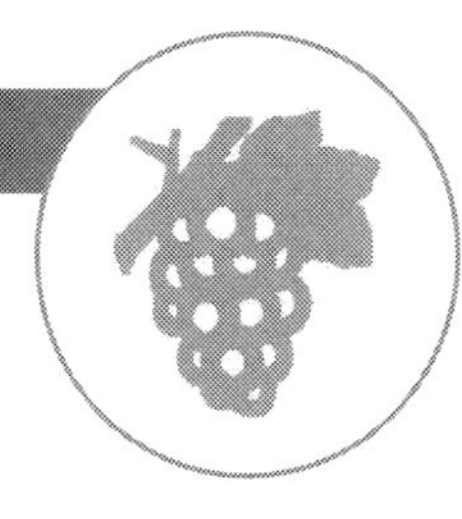

Ken Gire, in his book, *The Reflective Life*, suggests three habits that nurture a reflective life:

1. "Reading the moment (using our eyes to see what's on the surface).
2. Reflecting on the moment (engaging our mind to see what's beneath the surface).
3. Responding to the moment (giving what we have seen a place in our heart...allowing it to grow...upward to God and outward to other people)."[4]

Scripture Meditation

You may, at this point, want to spend a few minutes with a simple meditation on Scripture. The following selections from Scripture are suggested as a starting point:

"[M]y peace I give you" (John 14:27).

"Be still, and know that I am God" (Psalm 46:10).

"Now remain in my love" (John 15:9).

"I am the good shepherd" (John 10:11).

"Rejoice in the Lord always" (Philippians 4:4).

Spend a few minutes in meditation seeking to discover God near you, longing to encounter His presence. Take this opportunity to write a few notes about your experience below:

Additional Ideas for Personal Devotional Time

- Journaling: Many people keep a journal of what God is revealing through their times of devotion/reflection. The SOAP model is one way of doing this. This journal is also a good place to record prayer requests and answers.

- Praying your calendar: Some people find it helpful, especially when beginning the day with a devotional time, to pray through their calendar. As they consider the activities of the day, the people with whom they will interact, and the challenges they will face, this becomes a time to place all of those things before the throne of God.

- Examen: For those ending the day with a devotional time, a helpful practice is the prayer of examen - considering the activities of the day (e.g. imagine watching a video of your day) and developing an awareness of how God was present throughout the day. This aspect is called the examen of consciousness and includes a reflection on how we have responded to God. A second aspect is the examen of conscience in which we uncover our needs for cleansing, forgiveness, and healing.

Shared Worship Experiences

There are many ways groups can worship God together—from something as simple as saying grace before a meal, to such large-scale events as the televised funeral in the National Cathedral of a former President of the United States.

"Therefore, rid yourselves of all malice and all deceit, hypocrisy, envy, and slander of every kind. Like newborn babies, crave pure spiritual milk, so that by it you may grow up in your salvation." **I Peter 2:1-2**

Paul's Advice to the Church in Rome: Romans 12 (NRSV)

I appeal to you therefore, brothers and sisters, by the mercies of God, to present your bodies as a living sacrifice, holy and acceptable to God, which is your spiritual worship. Do not be conformed to this world, but be transformed by the renewing of your minds, so that you may discern what is the will of God—what is good and acceptable and perfect.

For by the grace given to me I say to everyone among you not to think of yourself more highly than you ought to think, but to think with sober judgment, each according to the measure of faith that God has assigned. For as in one body we have many members, and not all the members have the same function, so we, who are many, are one body in Christ, and individually we are members one of another. We have gifts that differ according to the grace given to us: prophecy, in proportion to faith; ministry, in ministering; the teacher, in teaching; the exhorter, in exhortation; the giver, in generosity; the leader, in diligence; the compassionate, in cheerfulness.

Let love be genuine; hate what is evil, hold fast to what is good; love one another with mutual affection; outdo one another in showing honor. Do not lag in zeal, be ardent in spirit, serve the Lord. Rejoice in hope, be patient in suffering, persevere in prayer. Contribute to the needs of the saints; extend hospitality to strangers.

Bless those who persecute you; bless and do not curse them. Rejoice with those who rejoice, weep with those who weep. Live in harmony with one another; do not be haughty, but associate with the lowly; do not claim to be wiser than you are. Do not repay anyone evil for evil, but take thought for what is noble in the sight of all. If it is possible, so far as it depends on you, live peaceably with all. Beloved, never avenge yourselves, but leave room for the wrath of God; for it is written, "Vengeance is mine, I will repay, says the Lord." No, "if your enemies are hungry, feed them; if they are thirsty, give them something to drink; for by doing this you will heap burning coals on their heads." Do not be overcome by evil, but overcome evil with good.

Sunday Services

There are several major styles of Sunday worship, each of which has its own variations:

"Liturgical Worship," with a set liturgy that is followed every Sunday, used in Catholic, Orthodox, Episcopalian, and Lutheran churches. Other churches, such as United Methodists, hold services like these only once a month. This is the oldest form of Christian worship and is based on the actions and words of Christ himself. The focus is centered on the Eucharist (Communion) and on the confession and forgiveness of sins. Liturgical worship seeks to engage all five senses, and everything in the service has some deeper symbolic meaning. Many participants find this a spiritually nourishing experience. They believe that it is through Communion that people receive God's grace and are empowered to live the life Christ revealed.

"Traditional Worship" is the term now used for the style of Sunday morning services used in the larger Protestant denominations, including United Methodists, Baptists, Presbyterians, Anabaptists, and many independent churches. The service usually emphasizes hearing, especially through the reading of Scripture, the sermon (often based on the Scripture reading), prayers, and singing. The service may also include other elements such as announcements, an altar call, or a baptism. The focus of these services is the Word, both as it is read and as it is discussed in the sermon. Singing is usually led by a choir and consists mostly of hymns from a published hymnal. These hymns often have deep theological meaning and may be unique to one

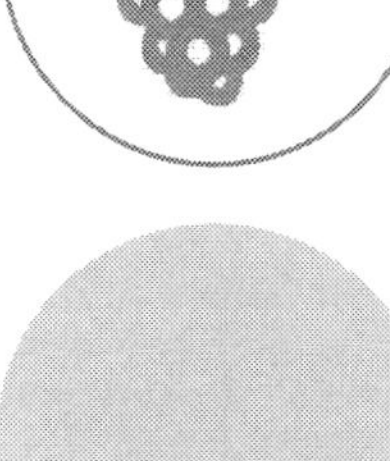

denomination. Many participants find this a spiritually uplifting experience. They believe that it is through hearing and understanding Scripture and reflections on Scripture that they can grow as Christians and come to a deeper understanding of God's love in their lives.

"Contemporary Worship" is a variation on traditional worship and has flourished in the same denominations, but has also led to the establishment of many nondenominational churches. It focuses on allowing contemporary popular culture to strongly influence worship services. It roots were in the 1950s, but it began to develop as a style in the 1960s and 1970s among youth movements. Whereas traditional worship focuses on the Word and uses old hymns and spirituals, contemporary worship focuses on new or recent songs that reflect contemporary culture. Rather than having a choir and congregational singing, this music is performed by a "praise band" with acoustic and electric instruments. The preference is for more informal settings than the traditional church's pews, altars, and pulpit. Wanting more comfortable seating arranged so the audience can see and hear the performers means some congregations prefer to meet in auditoriums or informal spaces. Stained glass windows, crosses, and images of Jesus or biblical passages are seen as unnecessary or even detrimental to encouraging non-Christians to feel at home. Because the repertoire changes often, there is no set hymnal. The words of songs may be projected onto a large screen for the participants to sing along with the band. Because these songs come from popular culture, they do not tend to have deeper theological meaning or to be specific to a denomination. The songs usually use informal language and focus on the intimate relationship between God and individuals. While there is quite a bit of variation in contemporary worship, the focus tends to be on the experience of praising God.

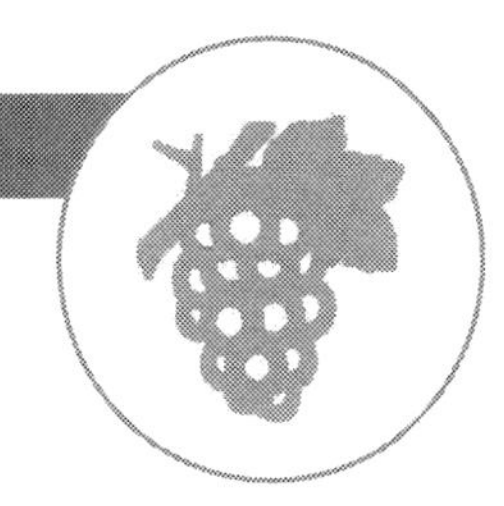

Dan Wakefield was a successful author and screenwriter who left Hollywood because the stressful lifestyle there was literally killing him. He moved back to his old neighborhood in Boston and began working on his physical health. Along the way he attended a Christian Unitarian-Universalist church for Christmas and Easter. After his health improved, he decided to think about other neglected aspects of his life.

He said, "I began to think again about church." He later wrote a book about his experience of ***Returning:***

My two initial trips of return had been on major holidays, occasions when "regular" people went to church, simply in observance of tradition. To go back again meant crossing the Boston Common on a non-holiday Sunday morning wearing a suit and tie, a giveaway sign of churchgoing. I did it furtively, as if I were engaged in something that would not be approved of by my peers. I hoped they would all be home doing brunch and the Sunday papers, so I would not be "caught in the act.". . .

To my surprise, I recognized neighbors and even some people I considered friends at church, on a "regular" Sunday. I had simply assumed I did not know people who went to church, yet here they were, with intellects intact, worshipping God. Once inside the church myself, I understood the appeal. No doubt my friends and neighbors found, as I did, relief and refreshment in connecting with age-old rituals, reciting psalms and singing hymns. There was a calm reassurance in the stately language of litanies and chants in the Book of Common Prayer (King's Chapel is "Unitarian in theology, Anglican in worship, and Congregational in governance," a historical Boston amalgam that became three centuries old in 1986). I was grateful for the sense of shared reverence, of reaching beyond one's flimsy physical presence, while praying with a whole congregation.

For Dan, the church quickly became more than a Sunday morning requirement. As troubles in his life continued to build, the church became a "sanctuary" for him "from the daily assaults of pressures and worries, the psychic guerrilla warfare of everyday life." He began attending Bible Study classes and then began leading them.

Bible study was not like examining history but like holding up a mirror to my own life, a mirror in which I sometimes saw things I was trying to keep hidden, even from myself. The first Scripture passage I was assigned to lead was from Luke, about the man who cleans his house of demons, and seven worse ones come. I did not have any trouble relating this to "contemporary life." It sounded unnervingly like an allegory about a man who had stopped drinking and so was enjoying much better health, but took up smoking marijuana to "relax," all the while feeling good and even self-righteous about giving up the booze. It was my own story. I realized, with a shock, how I'd been deceiving myself, how much more "housecleaning" I had to do.[5]

Developing a devotional life is just that...a lifestyle, not just a time. A devotional lifestyle begins with a time of devotion and expands into an awareness of the presence of God in all of life. Consider the following flow of behaviors that reflect a movement toward maturity:

Exploring: I attend worship when a friend invites me, it is convenient, or I feel a need

Beginning: I attend worship regularly, but am growing to realize that I must attend to God every day

Growing: I attend worship regularly and set aside time to connect with God daily through personal worship

Maturing: I live all of my life increasingly aware of God's presence and seeking to honor God

The practice (area) that I want to focus on developing is:

____

Someone who could support me in developing this is:

____

Resources that might be helpful:

____

1 Action Step:

When:

2 Action Step:

When:

The person who will partner with me:_____________________________

Wesley on the Powerful Connection Between Music and Worship

John Wesley's Methodist movement changed the way that disciples thought about music as it related to worship.

In the practices of the Anglican church at the time, music played a very different role in worship services. Wesley changed the way people used music—a change that had historically significant impacts.

- Wesley promoted congregational singing. In most worship services of the time, a choir performed religious music. Wesley believed in the power of people singing together.

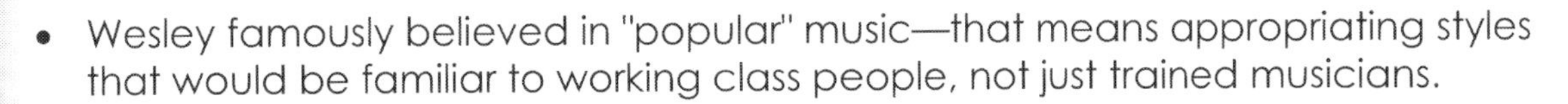

- Wesley famously believed in "popular" music—that means appropriating styles that would be familiar to working class people, not just trained musicians.
- Wesley believed in a hymnody that communicated theological truths. John Wesley, himself, composed only a handful of hymns. But his brother Charles composed hundreds (many of which are still sung today), and these hymns contained rich theological truths.
- Wesley had rules and recommendations (of course!) for how singing should happen in the local congregation. These were included in his introduction to the first Methodist hymnals. He had 10 such rules, but here are three of the most relevant for us:

1. Sing lustily and with good courage. Beware of singing as if you were half dead or half asleep, but lift up your voice with strength.

2. Sing modestly, but do not bawl, so as to be heard above or distinct from the rest of the congregation, that you may not destroy the harmony, but strive to unite your voices together.

3. Above all, sing spiritually. Have an eye toward God in every word you sing. Aim at pleasing him more than yourself or any other creature.

The Importance of the Lord's Supper

John Wesley focused on the power of the "means of grace " to deepen our connection to God. We have considered these means of grace in previous chapters (including prayer and Scripture reading), but equally significant was an emphasis on the Lord's Supper / Holy Communion / the Eucharist.

Wesley believed in receiving communion as often as possible, as he stated in his sermon, "The Duty of Constant Communion." He participated in communion at least once a week, and more than that when the opportunity presented itself.

Wesley believed in communion as a way to humbly remember Christ's sacrifice and to take hope in the prospect of renewal and the promise of the resurrection to come.

Wesley believed that communion connects us to the universal church, the fellowship of all who follow Christ around the world. This sacred remembrance is something all disciples share, regardless of denomination or other difference.

Communion is a holy sacrament. Wesley believed it to be a means of grace by which we are directly connected to the presence of Christ. Through it we willfully open our lives to the grace of God, and we believe him to be truly present in the elements. Through it we say yes to the Spirit's transforming power and we express our desire to be shaped by God's presence in the elements.

Wesley also introduced the idea of singing during communion. This was a distinct innovation for the time, introducing a layer of emotional and theological engagement. His brother, Charles, wrote many hymns for this purpose with lyrics such as these.

The cup of blessing, bless'd by thee,
let it thy blood impart;
the bread thy mystic body be,
and cheer each languid heart.
The grace which sure salvation brings,
let us herewith receive;
satiate the hungry with good things,
thy hidden manna give.

Jesus said to them, "Very truly I tell you, unless you eat the flesh of the Son of Man and drink his blood, you have no life in you. Whoever eats my flesh and drinks my blood has eternal life, and I will raise them up at the last day. For my flesh is real food and my blood is real drink. Whoever eats my flesh and drinks my blood remains in me, and I in them. Just as the living Father sent me and I live because of the Father, so the one who feeds on me will live because of me. This is the bread that came down from heaven. Your ancestors ate manna and died, but whoever feeds on this bread will live forever."
John 3:56-58

Building a Life of Service Through the Use of My Gifts and Talents

Service to others is an important part of discipleship. It is an opportunity for us to put our prayers and Scripture study into practice, to work together with our fellow disciples to do good in the world, and to live out the call to love our neighbors. Service can take many forms. We can serve others as individuals, meeting needs as we encounter them and giving of ourselves regularly to positively impact friends, neighbors, and complete strangers. We can team up with others to have an impact that is multiplied beyond what we can accomplish as a servant acting alone. God has given us unique gifts, talents, abilities, passions and experiences. These complementary characteristics equip us for the service to which we are called.

Let's start off by thinking about the ways you have already been of service to others. Make a list of ways that you have earned a living. What jobs have you held and what skills have you utilized in serving others through paid employment?

What ways have you volunteered your service? Make a list of the various volunteer positions you have held and the kinds of skills you have utilized in those volunteer positions.

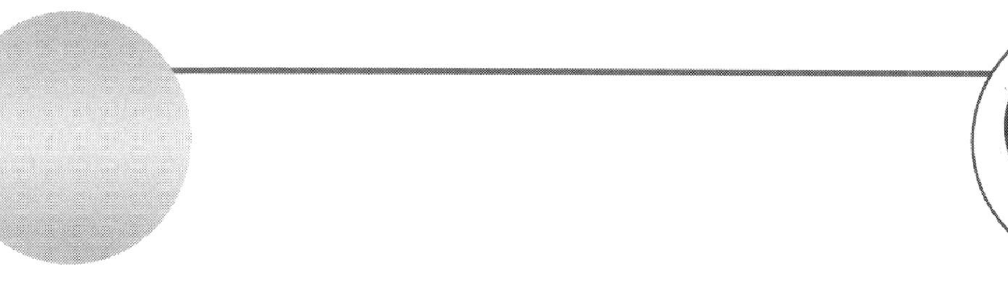

Now, go back to the last question and UNDERLINE the volunteer positions that you've held at church, CIRCLE the volunteer positions you've held that had nothing to do with church, and draw a BOX around the volunteer positions you've held that were because of (or coordinated by) your church but beyond the walls of the church. Which of those volunteer efforts are limited exclusively to the church environment and which involve skills that could be used anywhere? Analyze.

What are some skills that other people routinely tell you that you are very good at?

What are some skills that you admire in other people that you are convinced you are not good at?

Do you have an example of some time when you were talked into serving (or took a chance on serving) in a way that made you uncomfortable or ended in disaster?

What are movements, social justice issues, or topics in your community about which you feel great passion?

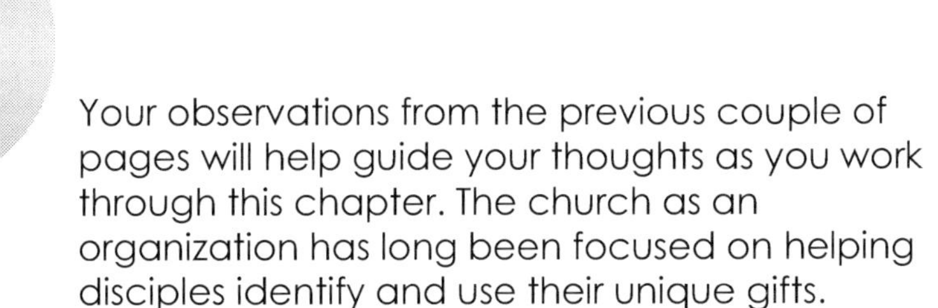

Your observations from the previous couple of pages will help guide your thoughts as you work through this chapter. The church as an organization has long been focused on helping disciples identify and use their unique gifts.

How Can a Church Be Organized Around Gifts and Talents?

I Corinthians 12 (NRSV)

Now concerning spiritual gifts, brothers and sisters, I do not want you to be uninformed. You know that when you were pagans, you were enticed and led astray to idols that could not speak. Therefore I want you to understand that no one speaking by the Spirit of God ever says "Let Jesus be cursed!" and no one can say "Jesus is Lord" except by the Holy Spirit.

Now there are varieties of gifts, but the same Spirit; and there are varieties of services, but the same Lord; and there are varieties of activities, but it is the same God who activates all of them in everyone. To each is given the manifestation of the Spirit for the common good. To one is given through the Spirit the utterance of wisdom, and to another the utterance of knowledge according to the same Spirit, to another faith by the same Spirit, to another gifts of healing by the one Spirit, to another the working of miracles, to another prophecy, to another the discernment of spirits, to another various kinds of tongues, to another the interpretation of tongues. All these are activated by one and the same Spirit, who allots to each one individually just as the Spirit chooses.

For just as the body is one and has many members, and all the members of the body, though many, are one body, so it is with Christ. For in the one Spirit we were all baptized into one body—Jews or Greeks, slaves or free—and we were all made to drink of one Spirit.

Indeed, the body does not consist of one member but of many. If the foot would say, "Because I am not a hand, I do not belong to the body," that would not make it any less a part of the body. And if the ear would say, "Because I am not an eye, I do not belong to the body," that would not make it any less a part of the body. If the whole body were an eye, where would the hearing be? If the whole body were hearing, where would the sense of smell be? But as it is, God arranged the members in the body, each one of them, as he chose. If all were a single member, where would the body be? As it is, there are many members, yet one body. The eye cannot say to the hand, "I have no need of you," nor again the head to the feet, "I have no need of you." On the contrary, the members of the body that seem to be weaker are indispensable, and those members of the body that we think less honorable we clothe with greater honor, and our less respectable members are treated with greater respect; whereas our more respectable members do not need this. But God has so arranged the body, giving the greater honor to the inferior member, that there may be no dissension within the body, but the members may have the same care for one another. If one member suffers, all suffer together with it; if one member is honored, all rejoice together with it.

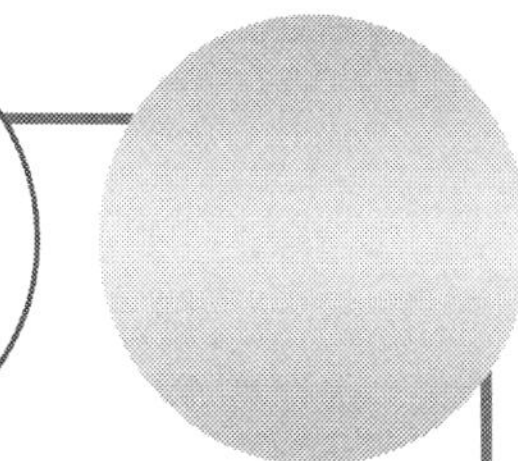

> Now you are the body of Christ and individually members of it. And God has appointed in the church first apostles, second prophets, third teachers; then deeds of power, then gifts of healing, forms of assistance, forms of leadership, various kinds of tongues. Are all apostles? Are all prophets? Are all teachers? Do all work miracles? Do all possess gifts of healing? Do all speak in tongues? Do all interpret? But strive for the greater gifts. And I will show you a still more excellent way (1 Corinthians 12, New Revised Standard Version).

In this text, Paul introduces the now familiar "body" image for the Christian community. This Scripture illustrates two different models of church organization and leadership. We call these the "Consumer" model and the "Biblical" model.

The Consumer Model is based around the idea that the pastor and staff are employed to minister to the needs of the congregation. Some key understandings for this perspective include:

- There is one Minister or a staff of Ministers identified by the local congregation as responsible for conducting ministry.
- That Minister or staff of Ministers is hired by the congregation to serve the congregation (e.g. preach, teach, visit the sick, etc.).
- It is an inward-focused style of ministry. The focus of the ministry is on caring for the needs of the members of the congregation.
- It has a limited scope. Since the ministry of the congregation is centered around the ministry of one individual Minister or staff of Ministers, the number of people served is limited to the time and abilities of the person or persons filling that role.
- It is a ministry by virtue of education. The persons filling the role of Minister are brought into that position by virtue of their specific training for ministry through seminary or Bible college.
- It is a ministry by job description. The persons filling the role of Minister have a specific description of responsibilities identified by the congregation that must be accomplished regardless of personal abilities or even specific training.

The Biblical Model has a very different understanding:

- Ministry by virtue of baptism: This model affirms that through baptism each of us is gifted and ordained by the Holy Spirit to participate in the ministry of the Kingdom.
- Congregation of Ministers: Rather than one minister or a staff of ministers being hired to serve the congregation, this model recognizes that the congregation is made up of lay ministers called to serve and meet the needs of one another as well as those in the community and world.
- Pastor/Staff are hired to equip the congregation for ministry. This is a major paradigm shift in understanding the role of pastors and staff. Rather than being hired to serve, their role is to train up the congregation for ministry.
- Outward focused: In contrast to the chaplaincy model where the focus is on meeting the needs of the members, this model directs the members into ministry in the world around them.
- Unlimited Scope: In this model, the potential for ministry is basically unlimited. While a chaplain can only meet the needs of a finite number of people, a congregation full of ministers can reach an almost unlimited number. For example, let's say a Minister (chaplain style) can effectively minister to the needs of 100 people. If those 100 people were empowered for ministry and provided ministry for only 10 persons each, that's a ten-fold increase in the scope of ministry!
- Ministry by Gifts: This model recognizes that every believer is gifted by the Holy Spirit to be part of the ministry of the Kingdom. Rather than degrees and certificates indicating some level of competency, the emphasis falls on discovering how God has gifted us for ministry and then using those gifts as God intended.

How Can I Recognize My Gifts and Talents?

One way is to take a Spiritual Gifts Inventory. Often, your local church will have such an inventory that they will provide you with. If so, access it and complete it.

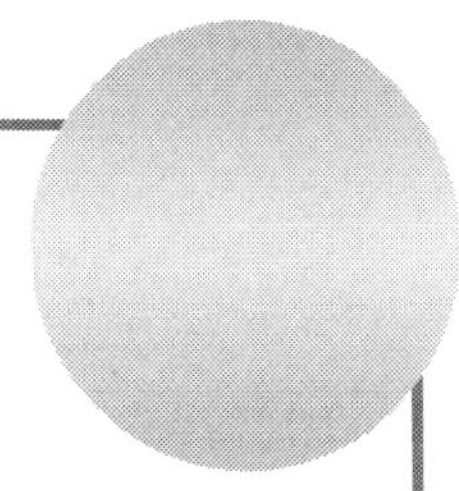

Or go directly to the questionnaire page here:

umcdiscipleship.org/spiritual-gifts-inventory.

Follow the instructions and fill out the questionnaire. Your results will come up at the end of the questionnaire. By clicking on each gift shown in blue lettering with an underline, you can see a description of that gift.

Keep in mind that no one gift is more important than another. This exercise is to see the diversity of gifts God has given us, not to set one person or ministry above others.

If you cannot access the website, read the following descriptions and arrange them in the order of your strengths and abilities as best you can.

A Descriptive List of Spiritual Gifts

Administration: "The gift of administration allows a person to organize people and resources for greater efficiency, effectiveness, and success. Administrators have the natural ability to apply resources where they will do the greatest good. Administrators are good with details and are deeply aware of how all the parts of a group or organization work together to achieve their goals."

Apostleship: "The gift of apostleship compels people to reach out to new and unfamiliar groups and individuals to invite them into relationship with God and community. Apostles share the story of faith in other lands, cultures, and traditions, as well as welcoming the stranger in their own land. Apostles extend the hand of friendship to those of other generations, nations, and languages. Many apostles desire to be missionaries."

Compassion: "The gift of compassion moves people to action on behalf of those in need. Compassion is not a simple caring about others, but such a radical caring that we have no choice but to make sacrifices for others. Those with the gift of compassion rarely ask '*Should* I help?' but instead focus on *how* to help. Compassion makes us fundamentally aware of the Christ in others and springs from our desire to care for all of God's creatures and creation."

Discernment: "Discernment is a gift of deep intuition and insight. Discerning people can separate truth from fiction and know at a visceral level when people are being honest. Deeply sensitive and "tuned in," those with the gift of discernment are open to feelings, new ideas, and intuition as valid and credible information. Discernment is not irrational, but transrational—beyond empirical—knowledge."

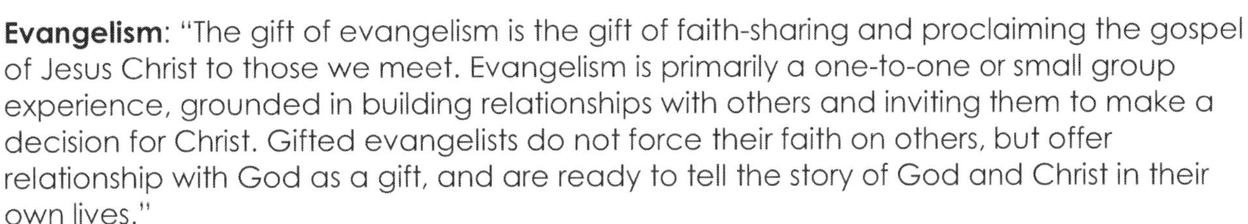

Evangelism: "The gift of evangelism is the gift of faith-sharing and proclaiming the gospel of Jesus Christ to those we meet. Evangelism is primarily a one-to-one or small group experience, grounded in building relationships with others and inviting them to make a decision for Christ. Gifted evangelists do not force their faith on others, but offer relationship with God as a gift, and are ready to tell the story of God and Christ in their own lives."

Exhortation: "The gift of exhortation is manifest in people who offer encouragement, wise counsel, unflagging support, and empowerment. Those who exhort stay focused on helping people maximize their own potential and live from their own gifts and skills. Exhorters help people feel good about themselves, build confidence, and not grow discouraged. Often, those with the gift of exhortation make others feel good just by being present."

Faith: "The gift of faith is more than belief in Jesus Christ, but an abiding foundation of confidence that God works all things together for good, and that the people of God can rise above any obstacle. Faith is the bedrock upon which we build lives, congregations, and communities. People with the gift of faith hold fast to the deep conviction that no matter what we see with our eyes, we can trust the promises and plan of God."

Giving: "The gift of giving is the deep commitment to provide whatever resources are needed to support God's will and plan. In addition to radical generosity, those who possess the gift of giving have the uncanny ability to discover and channel new sources of money, time, and energy to needs. Money management skills, grant writing abilities, and the easy knack of asking for donations and cultivating donors are among common skills of gifted givers."

Healing: "The gift of healing is not about transferring spiritual power to eliminate suffering and disease, but the ability to channel God's grace and healing love to those who suffer physical, emotional, or spiritual pain. Healers are moved to be present with those who suffer. Healers pray for those who suffer, visit those who are ill, and are usually moved to extend a hand of comfort and touch to those who are afflicted. Healers give their time and energy to offering aid and comfort to others."

Helping: "Helping is a gift of support and behind-the-scenes effort that make groups, families, and congregations more effective. Not everyone is gifted to lead, but many are gifted to follow and handle the tasks that are so essential, but less glamorous. Helpers love to serve others, support others, and assist others in the important work of ministry and mission. Tireless in their willingness to serve, helpers are less interested in receiving thanks and recognition than in doing good, valuable work."

Interpretation: "Those who are gifted to interpret tongues help build bridges across cultural, generational, and language divides. People who possess this gift have an innate ability to learn new languages and cultural practices, and can help others understand them as well. Foreign-speaking people are attracted to those with this gift, and feel intuitively that they will be better understood and received by interpreters. Interpretation breaks down barriers."

Knowledge: "The gift of knowledge allows people to automatically convert facts, data, and information into useful and important knowledge. People possessing this gift can learn in a variety of ways, retain what they learn, and understand how learning can be applied in meaningful and productive ways. Those gifted with knowledge have a voracious and insatiable desire to learn more, and they seek multiple avenues for deepening their understanding of God's world, God's will, and God's people."

Leadership: "The gift of leadership is a visionary and forward-looking gift that enables people to stay focused on where God might be leading us as individuals, congregations, and communities at any given time. Leaders look more to where we are going rather than where we currently are or where we have been. Leaders motivate others to work together in ways that help them achieve more together than any could on their own. Leaders provide examples of how we should order our lives to honor and glorify God."

Miracles: "The gift of miracles is not about performing miracles, but about living in the miraculous reality of God's creation. Those gifted with miracles never doubt the power and presence of God in creation, and are able to help others see and believe in God's power. The gift of miracles does not focus on the extraordinary, but sees the miraculous in the mundane and normal. Living in the spirit of the miraculous, people see God in nature, in relationships, in kind acts, and in the power of love."

Prophecy: "The gift of prophecy is the ability to speak God's word to others, or more appropriately to be open for God to speak God's word through us. Prophets do not predict the future, but offer insight and perspective on current conditions and how things might turn out if changes aren't made. Prophets are incisive, clear, and often controversial communicators. Prophets see things that others often don't, and they have the courage to 'tell it like it ought to be.'"

Servanthood: "Servanthood is the gift of doing for others, sometimes to the exclusion of meeting personal needs. Servants look for ways to do for others both within and beyond the congregation and community. Servants do not choose to serve, but serve from a sense of identity and call. Gifted servants never feel put-upon or taken advantage of, but see each opportunity to do for others as a way to be true to self."

Shepherding: "The gift of shepherding is the gift of mentoring and providing spiritual guidance to others to help them develop in the discipleship and faith formation. Shepherds take an active and individualized interest in the life of faith of others. Shepherds share from their own faith journey to make the way easier for others. Shepherds are good at asking provocative questions, recommending appropriate resources and experiences, and helping people find their own way to the next level of their development."

Teaching: "The gift of teaching allows people to transform data and information into life-changing knowledge. Teachers do not have to stand in front of a class to teach. Often gifted teachers communicate best in informal, one-on-one settings. Teachers have the uncanny knack of helping people learn effortlessly. People internalize and retain the knowledge and learning they receive from gifted teachers. Good teachers transform more than they inform."

Tongues: "The gift of tongues is a communication gift that allows people to speak foreign languages and convey concepts they never formally studied. People with this gift 'pick up' the ability to communicate across barriers of language, culture, age, or physical limitation (some people with the gift of tongues work with the deaf or blind). The gift of tongues is not a 'secret' prayer language, but a way to communicate the faith to people in a known language."

Wisdom: "The gift of wisdom allows people to understand deeper meaning and apply knowledge, beliefs, and experience to everyday situations. Wise, gifted individuals make connections and help others make them as well—to understand the implications of our beliefs and actions. Those gifted with wisdom often understand root causes of disagreements, conflict, and barriers to growth and development. People with wisdom help others understand and clarify options to make good decisions."

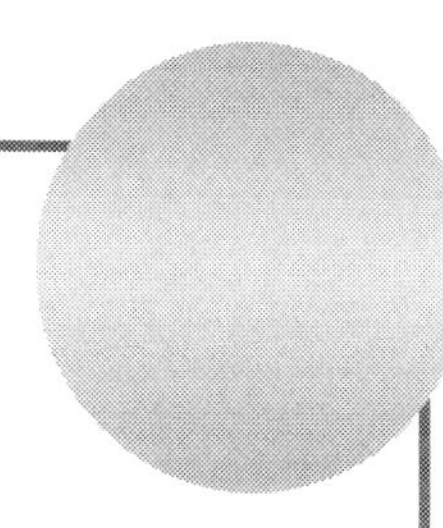

Unpacking the Spiritual Gifts Inventory:

List below your top three spiritual gifts according to the inventory. Read the definitions for each of those gifts. Then, describe briefly how you may have seen those gifts at work in you without realizing it.

-
-
-

Seven Basic Principles of Spiritual Gifts

- Spiritual gifts are given to the believer by the Holy Spirit.
- Spiritual gifts are given to every believer without exception.
- Spiritual gifts are gifts of God's grace.
- The Spirit gives diverse gifts for a diversity of ministries.
- Spiritual gifts are to be employed for building up the Body of Christ.
- Gifted believers are part of the Body of Christ.
- Gifts must always be used in Love.

Scriptures Related to Spiritual Gifts

The following passages are related to the identification and application of spiritual gifts. Read through them and identify the Seven Principles of Spiritual Gifts as they appear.

I Corinthians 12:8-10

I Corinthians 12:28

Romans 12:6-8

Ephesians 4:11

I Peter 4:9-10

Exodus 31:3

I Timothy 2:1-2

S.H.A.P.E.

The Spiritual Gifts Inventory is just one tool for exploring how God has wired us for ministry. Rick Warren, pastor at Saddleback Community Church in California, suggests the S.H.A.P.E paradigm for exploring more fully how we are wired.

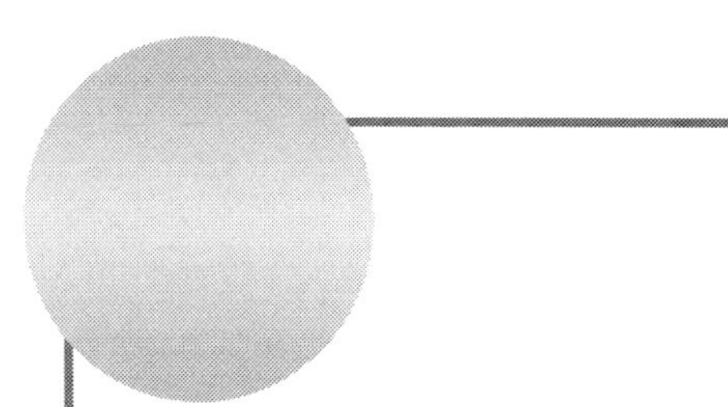

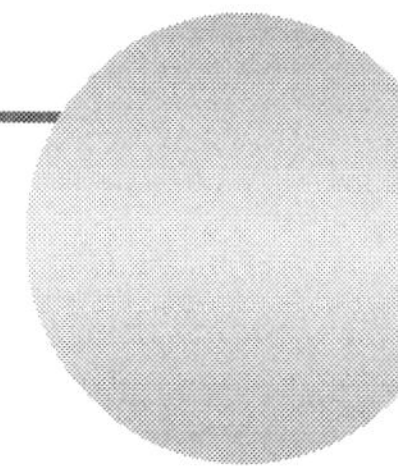

What's Your S.H.A.P.E.?[2]

Spiritual Gifts: What are your gifts (identified by inventory)?

Heart: What is your passion? (e.g. homeless, abused, working poor, education, etc.)

Abilities: What are you good at doing? How are you talented?

Personality: Do you work best in front of crowds, one-on-one, or by yourself? Do you build a plan or just "go for it"?

Experiences: What life experiences have shaped who you are?

The discipleship journey is about outward behaviors that reflect the inner grace as we move toward maturity. In the area of service, a movement toward maturity might look like this:

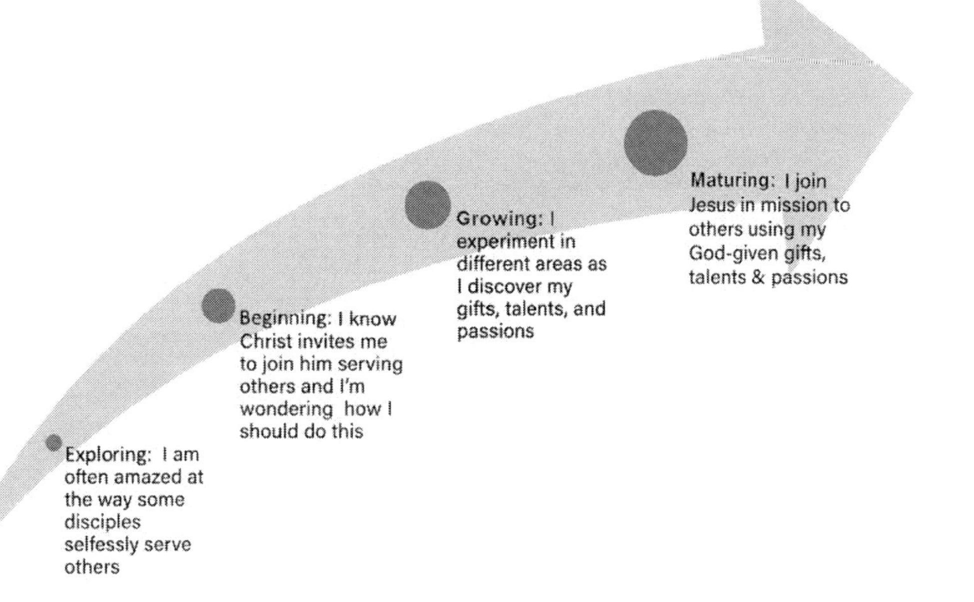

The practice (area) that I want to focus on developing is:

____

Someone who could support me in developing this is:

____

Resources that might be helpful:

____

1 Action Step:

When:

2 Action Step:

When:

The person who will partner with me:_______________

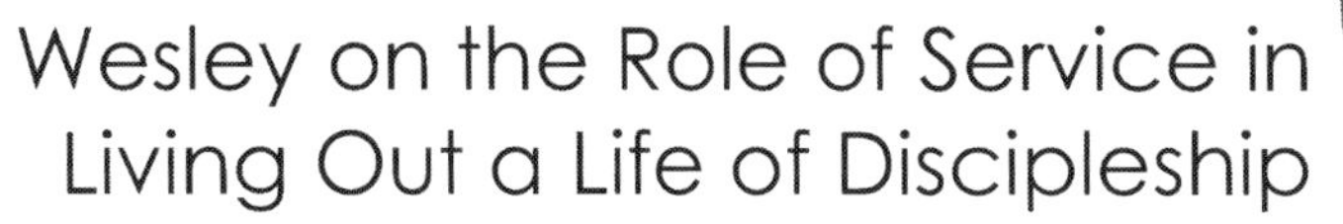

Wesley on the Role of Service in Living Out a Life of Discipleship

In 1739, a group of Christians approached John Wesley in London, having been inspired by his lessons and leadership and deeply concerned about their spiritual state, and asked that he provide them with additional guidance. He agreed, and the gathering that followed evolved into the first Society. Addressing a need to form a clear set of expectations for this accountability group—and the many Societies that were to follow—Wesley devised the General Rules for participation. These rules of agreed-upon conduct involved prayer, Bible study, regular fellowship and other aspects of discipleship, but they also were direct in their expectation that Society members would "love their neighbors as themselves."

The General Rules (as applied to Service)

- **First, do no harm.** Many of the rules that Wesley listed involved conducting oneself in such a way as to prevent active harm to others (or the reputation of the followers of Christ). Many of these are still applicable: no fighting or quarreling, no seeking vengeance, no taking advantage of others, no speaking ill of others, no drunkenness, no wastefulness, no ostentatious displays of wealth, and no laziness. Some of the provisions reflect the concerns of an earlier historical era: no slave-holding, no lending of money for interest, no popular entertainment that does not directly glorify God. The general concept was based on a variation in a familiar verse from Scripture: "Don't do something to someone else that you wouldn't want them to do to you" (Matthew 7:12 paraphrase).
- **Secondly, do as much good as possible:** "By being in every kind merciful after their power; as they have opportunity, doing good of every possible sort, and, as far as possible, to all men." This meant following Jesus' directive in Matthew 25 to feed the hungry, clothe the naked, and visit or help the sick and those in prison. Wesley also included a general provision that basically reminded disciples that their daily actions are a reflection on Christ, and he encouraged Christians to support one another by doing business with one another and hiring fellow Christians (a provision that might lead to some interesting discussion today).

On Social Justice

Methodists have a history of activism

John Wesley was deeply engaged in the social issues of the day. While we generally think of 'service' as acting in mercy and charity (meeting the immediate needs of people), Wesley and United Methodism have a long history of engaging the root causes of human suffering and struggle through advocating for societal change, including actively embracing broad social movements and working for changes in government policy. Wesley, himself, was personally involved in important issues of his era:

- Prison reform
- Human rights
- Substance abuse
- Workers' rights
- Economic justice
- Healthcare
- Slavery (still relevant in today's world, particularly in regards to human trafficking)

Do all the good you can, to all the people you can, in all the ways you can, as long as ever you can. -- John Wesley

The Methodist Episcopal Church adopted the first official Social Creed in 1908, largely in response to repressive labor conditions of the time. This creed has been updated and included in the Book of Discipline in the decades since and expanded upon with the creation of a collection of Social Principles.

Some excerpts from the Social Creed:

- On the natural world: "We affirm the natural world as God's handiwork and dedicate ourselves to its preservation, enhancement, and faithful use by humankind."
- On accessibility: "We commit ourselves to the rights of men, women, children, youth, young adults, the aging, and people with disabilities; to improvement of the quality of life; and to the rights and dignity of all persons."
- On economic security: "We believe in the right and duty of persons to work for the glory of God and the good of themselves and others and in the protection of their welfare in so doing; in the rights to property as a trust from God, collective bargaining, and responsible consumption; and in the elimination of economic and social distress."
- On peace and justice: "We dedicate ourselves to peace throughout the world, to the rule of justice and law among nations, and to individual freedom for all people of the world."

And on the attitude all disciples should display in achieving these goals: "We believe in the present and final triumph of God's Word in human affairs and gladly accept our commission to manifest the life of the gospel in the world. Amen."

Building a Life of Generosity Through Stewardship

One of the clearest windows as to our priorities is how we spend (and choose not to spend) our money. Our financial resources are a gift from God, and the ways that we use those resources reveals much about our fears, anxieties, aspirations, and obsessions. Honestly answer the following questions as a precursor to thinking about your approach to stewardship.

Am I treating God as owner and CEO/CFO of "my" assets, or am I treating God merely as my financial consultant, whom maybe I pay a fee in consideration of His services (an occasional tip or 2%, 5% or 10%)?

Do I have an intentional strategy for my "ministry of generosity"? Do I have a strategic plan for giving? A specific budget?

How comfortable am I talking about finances, budgeting, stewardship and giving? If I am married, do I share good communication and a common vision with my spouse? If I have kids, in what specific ways am I teaching them to be responsible stewards and lead a life of generosity?

What aspects of talking about finances, budgeting, stewardship, and generosity am I most uncomfortable discussing with others? Do I seek advice and guidance from those wiser than me (and those farther along the path of discipleship)?

For you, how much money would be enough? Specifically? If you could own just five things (other than a house and a car), what would they be?

Numbers Speak Truth about Priorities

What are my three biggest recurring payments each month? (In general terms, what are the three biggest bills for which I consistently write a check? Back when we all wrote checks, that is!) House payment? Car payment? Tithes or ministry gifts? Health insurance? Tuition? Entertainment?

What is your budget for eating out every month? (If you can't give a reasonably specific number to a question like this, financial experts would point out this is an indication of undisciplined impulse spending, as opposed to living within a budget.)

What would you say your greatest budget indulgence is? Something you know is unessential, maybe even frivolous, that brings you joy? Make a case for why this expenditure is important.

Describe a time when you gave sacrificially to a cause. What motivated you? What did you sacrifice? How did this decision for generosity make you feel?

If you won a million dollars in the lottery tomorrow, how would you spend it? Write down specific allocations for this windfall.

The questions from the previous two pages can help us be honest about our attitudes towards earning money, spending money, and sharing money.

For disciples of Jesus, we are not just making these decisions based on our own preferences. The Bible gives us clear guidance in how to proceed if we are to experience maximum joy and purpose.

Generosity and Stewardship in Relationships

Throughout this study we have been talking about Christianity in terms of relationships and how to build and develop better relationships: Our relationships within our families, our relationship with God the Father, our relationship with Christ, and our relationship with others. Let's take a little time to think about how to safeguard those relationships…from ourselves.

Relationships take time and attention. Building strong relationships is a challenge in our society. It takes real work. There are many ways to strengthen them, but there are also many ways to weaken them.

"Believers in humble circumstances ought to take pride in their high position. But the rich should take pride in their humiliation—since they will pass away like a wild flower. For the sun rises with scorching heat and withers the plant; its blossom falls and its beauty is destroyed. In the same way, the rich will fade away even while they go about their business."
James 1:9-11

Giving our devotion to money, power, and things damages relationships. "Spending" our time "keeping up with the Joneses" takes our time and attention away from our relationships. "Spending" our time rushing around from one thing to another keeps us from attending to God and what He has told us to do.

Simplicity and Generosity

Richard Foster, author of the classic book *Celebration of Discipline,* writes about financial stewardship under the theme of 'simplicity,' stating:

> *"Simplicity is the only thing that sufficiently reorients our lives so that possessions can be genuinely enjoyed without destroying us…Simplicity sets us free to receive the provision of God as a gift that is not ours to keep and can be freely shared with others."*[1]

How does this quote from Foster speak to you?

What are the implications for our lives?

The Cultural Struggles of Affluenza: We struggle in leading lives of simplicity. Some students of our culture have described our condition using the word, 'Affluenza.' Affluenza is a confluence of two words: the word 'affluence' and the word 'influenza.' The point these cultural observers are making is that it is normal in our society to be infected by affluence—to have a dysfunctional relationship with money, things, and others. What does that mean? At least these three things: materialism, consumerism, and easy debt.

- **Materialism**: The first thing *Affluenza* suggests is that our culture is characterized by materialism. In short, materialism means that it is all about the stuff. As the quip goes: "He who dies with the most toys wins." In our culture, it is normal for people to seek their sense of purpose, fulfillment, self-esteem, and security based on the stuff they have managed to collect. Hebrews 13:5 warns us about the idolatry of stuff: "Keep your lives free from the love of money and be content with what you have, because God has said, 'Never will I leave you; never will I forsake you.'"

Take a few moments to think about how you feel about money and the 'things' in your life. How are you affected by the materialism of our culture?

- **Consumerism**: The second thing *Affluenza* suggests is that our culture is characterized by consumerism. Consumerism is about consuming more and more and more stuff. How much is enough money? How much is enough stuff? Most people in our culture—no matter how much they already have—answer, "I need more!" How many more shirts do you need? How many more shoes? "More." And yet, if all of the people in the world consumed as much stuff as normal Westerners consume, it would take not one, not two, not three, but four planets the size of earth to sustain it. Our current rate of consumption is simply not eco-sustainable – and yet we normally believe that our sense of contentment and fulfillment depends on consuming…more. The cathedrals of our culture are shopping malls, and advertisers are the priests. According to the writer of Ecclesiastes 5:10, "Whoever loves money never has enough; whoever loves wealth is never satisfied with their income."

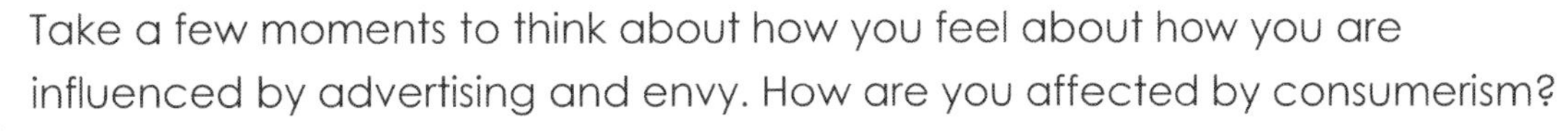

Take a few moments to think about how you feel about how you are influenced by advertising and envy. How are you affected by consumerism?

- **Easy Debt**: And so we continue working and buying more stuff until we can afford no more, based on what we make and have financially. Not to worry though, because our culture makes it easy for us to purchase more stuff on credit. Easy debt is the third characteristic of Affluenza. Over 60% of families do not pay off their credit cards each month. And no wonder: Studies show that people using plastic spend 12–18% more than when using cash. When McDonald's decided to accept credit cards, the average ticket jumped a staggering 47% from $4.75 to $7.00.[2] Being in debt has become normal in our Affluenza-infected culture. It's as if people were infected with 'credit-itis,' as Adam Hamilton calls it in *Enough*.[3] Many people struggling with significant consumer debt recognize the truth of Proverbs 22:7, "The rich rule over the poor, and the borrower is slave to the lender." Excessive debt can literally reverse the Exodus and make people prisoners of living beyond their means.

Take a few moments to think about how you feel about the acessibility of credit and the pressure to "buy now, pay later." How are you and your family affected by easy debt?

But godliness with contentment is great gain. For we brought nothing into the world, and we can take nothing out of it. But if we have food and clothing, we will be content with that. Those who want to get rich fall into temptation and a trap and into many foolish and harmful desires that plunge people into ruin and destruction. For the love of money is a root of all kinds of evil. Some people, eager for money, have wandered from the faith and pierced themselves with many griefs."

I Timothy 6:6-10

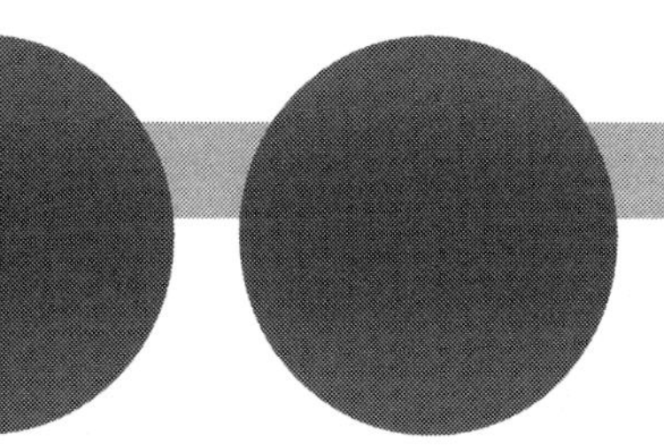

Foundational Spiritual Principles of Money Management:

- God is the *owner.*
- We are the *managers.*
- God has the *rights* to all that God owns.
- Every financial decision is a *spiritual decision.*
- We are ultimately *accountable* to God for our *money* management.

Why God asks us to give:

- It reminds us who is the owner and who is the manager.
- Giving demands faith. It puts our heart in a relationship of dependence and trust.
- Giving positions our heart.
- Giving lets us experience the thrill of making a difference.

Biblical Principles of Financial Management

Read the following verses and write down the biblical principle of stewardship each relates.

Malachi 3:8-10: *"Will a mere mortal rob God? Yet you rob me. But you ask, 'How are we robbing you?' In tithes and offerings. You are under a curse—your whole nation—because you are robbing me. Bring the whole tithe into the storehouse, that there may be food in my house. Test me in this," says the LORD Almighty, "and see if I will not throw open the floodgates of heaven and pour out so much blessing that there will not be room enough to store it."*

Biblical Principle of Stewardship: ______________________________

I Corinthians 16:1-2: *"Now about the collection for the Lord's people: Do what I told the Galatian churches to do. On the first day of every week, each one of you should set aside a sum of money in keeping with your income, saving it up, so that when I come no collections will have to be made."*

Biblical Principle of Stewardship: ______________________________

II Corinthians 9:7: *"Each of you should give what you have decided in your heart to give, not reluctantly or under compulsion, for God loves a cheerful giver."*

Biblical Principle of Stewardship: ______________________________

Some other basic biblical principles related to financial management:

- Avoid *unnecessary* debt: *"The rich rule over the poor, and the borrower is slave to the lender"* (Proverbs 22:7).
- Seek counsel: *"The way of fools seems right to them, but the wise listen to advice"* (Proverbs 12:15).
- *Save* for the future: *"The wise man saves for the future, but the foolish man spends whatever he gets"* (Proverbs 21:20, The Living Bible).
- Learn to be *content*: *"For I have learned to be content in whatever circumstances I am. I know how to get along with humble means, and I also know how to live in prosperity; in any and every circumstance I have learned the secret of being filled and going hungry, both of having abundance and suffering need. I can do all things through him who strengthens me"* (Philippians 4:11-13, New American Standard Bible).
- *Teach* your children how to handle money: *"Train up a child in the way he should go, even when he is old he will not depart from it"* (Proverbs 22:6, New American Standard Bible).

What God wants for us financially

- Gratitude: *"Give thanks to the Lord, for he is good; his love endures forever. Cry out, 'Save us, God our Savior…that we may give thanks to your holy name, and glory in your praise'"* (I Chronicles 16:34-35).
- Contentment: *"Keep your lives free from the love of money and be content with what you have, because God has said, 'Never will I leave you, never will I forsake you'"* (Hebrews 13:5).
- Compassion: *"Anyone who has been stealing must steal no longer, but must work, doing something useful with their own hands, that they may have something to share with those in need"* (Ephesians 4:28).
- Generosity: *"But a Samaritan, as he traveled, came where the man was; and when he saw him, he took pity on him. He went to him and bandaged his wounds, pouring on oil and wine. Then he put the man on his own donkey, brought him to an inn and took care of him. The next day he took out two denarii and gave them to the innkeeper. 'Look after him,' he said, 'and when I return, I will reimburse you for any extra expense you may have'"* (Luke 10:33-35).

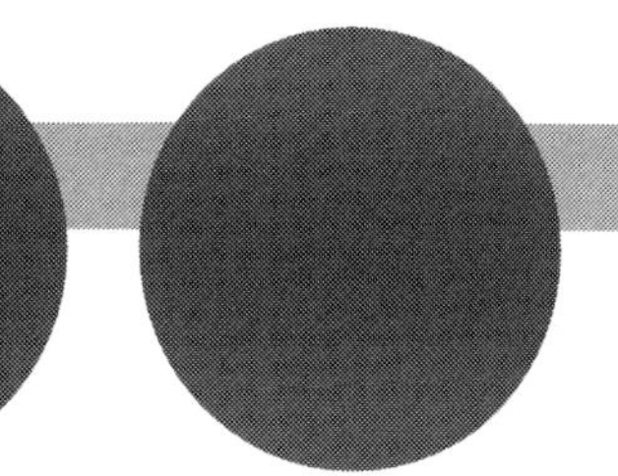

How do we live into God's plan?

- The journey to faithful financial stewardship begins with the recognition that everything we have and everything we are belong 100% to God, followed by a decision on our part to use all our resources in ways that are pleasing to God.
- The second step is to adjust our lifestyle so that we are living on less than we actually earn. We call this 'living with margin.' This idea is found way back in the Old Testament Scriptures. For example, in Leviticus:

"When you reap the harvest of your land, do not reap to the very edges of your field or gather the gleanings of your harvest. Do not go over your vineyard a second time or pick up the grapes that have fallen. Leave them for the poor and the foreigner" (Leviticus 19:9-10).

Consider the following uses for the resources not utilized when living with margins:

Eliminate Debt
Establish an Emergency Fund
Create an Educational Fund
Build Savings
Plan for Retirement
Support God's Causes (including our tithe)

- Be as generous as you can in the ways that God leads you!

Some give freely, yet grow all the richer;
others withhold what is due, and only suffer want.
A generous person will be enriched,
and one who gives water will get water.
The people curse those who hold back grain, but
a blessing is on the head of those who sell it.
Whoever diligently seeks good seeks favor,
but evil comes to the one who searches for it.
Those who trust in their riches will wither,
but the righteous will flourish like green leaves.

Proverbs 11:24-28 (NRSV)

Many congregations have come to realize that it is not enough to ask disciples of Jesus to tithe. We often have overcommitted ourselves financially (leaving no margin) and need to learn how to live differently. How does your congregation or community support those seeking to become stronger financial stewards?

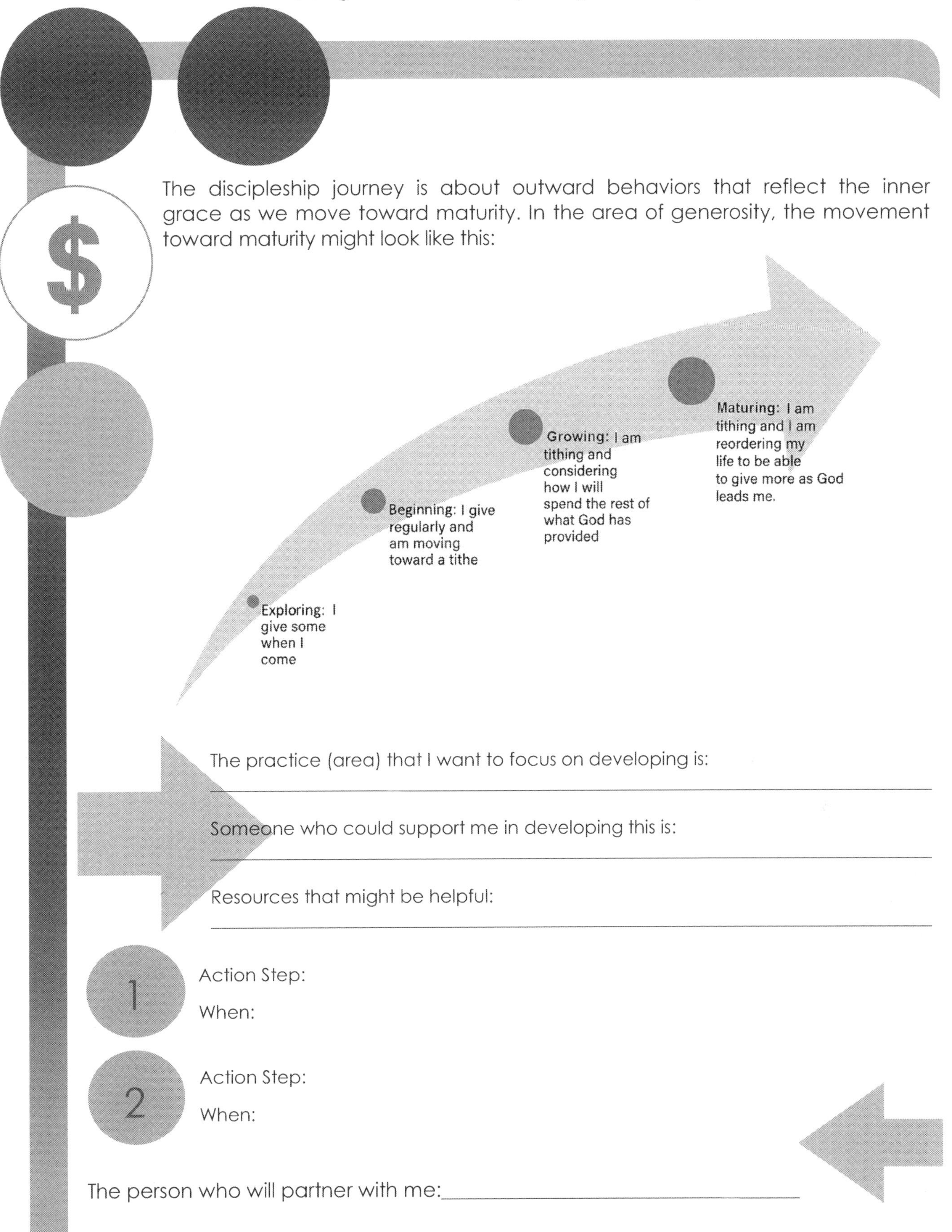

The discipleship journey is about outward behaviors that reflect the inner grace as we move toward maturity. In the area of generosity, the movement toward maturity might look like this:

The practice (area) that I want to focus on developing is: ______________________

Someone who could support me in developing this is: ______________________

Resources that might be helpful: ______________________

Action Step:

When:

Action Step:

When:

The person who will partner with me: ______________________

John Wesley on Stewardship

The power of "Earn, Save, Give" as a guiding philosophy

In "Thoughts Upon Methodism," John Wesley articulated his principles for stewardship and living a lifestyle of generosity in a formulation that has held up through vast changes in economic systems:

"What way, then, (I ask again) can we take, that our money may not sink us to the nethermost hell? There is one way, and there is no other under heaven. If those who 'gain all they can,' and 'save all they can,' will likewise 'give all they can;' then, the more they gain, the more they will grow in grace, and the more treasure they will lay up in heaven."

- *Earn all you can.*
- *Save all you can.*
- *Give all you can.*

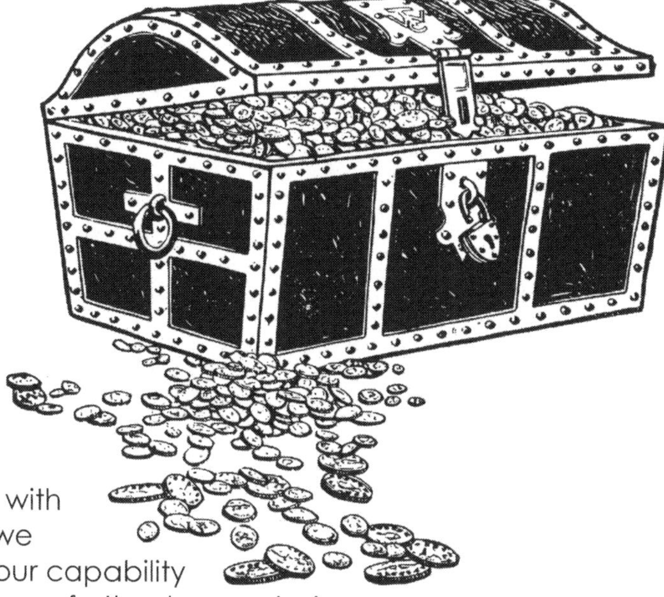

He fleshed these principles out more fully in a sermon titled, "The Use of Money."

In encouraging his flock to **earn all you can**, he stressed the values of hard work in the service of godly principles, not attaining money by any nefarious means possible, but by working honestly, serving others with integrity and compassion, so that we gain the material resources within our capability but not at the expense of the welfare of other human beings.

In challenging his fellow disciples to **save all you can**, he was not an advocate for hoarding what we have earned or even locking maximum sums away in grand investment schemes for some far off retirement future. He really was preaching about living a frugal lifestyle, saving as much as possible through saying a firm "no" to materialism and waste.

In encouraging his fellow disciples to **give all you can**, he showed how the earning and saving empowers us to live generously, because living generously is how our lives reflect God's character in the world. God is generous. Therefore, we are generous as an acknowledgment and response to that divine template.

Wesley Practiced What He Preached

"(Money) is an excellent gift of God, answering the noblest ends. In the hands of his children, it is food for the hungry, drink for the thirsty, raiment for the naked. It gives to the traveler and the stranger where to lay his head. By it we may supply the place of a husband to the widow, and of a father for the fatherless; we may be a defense for the oppressed, a means of health to the sick, of ease to them that are in pain. It may be as eyes to the blind, as feet to the lame; yea, a lifter up from the gates of death."

–John Wesley from "Notes on Money"

Wesley's personal journey with this topic greatly influenced his public teaching. The story is told of the epiphany he had as a 31-year-old student at Oxford when, having just proudly purchased some pictures for his room, he noticed the chambermaid had nothing to protect her from the winter cold other than a thin gown. His impulse was to hand her some money for a coat from his own coat pocket, but he had none to offer, having just spent it on wall decor. From that point on, he made it a point to live on as little as possible, earning £30 that year, but living off £28, so he had £2 to give away.

Here's the astonishing thing: although his income doubled, tripled, and eventually grew to as much as £1,400 yearly, he continued to give it all away each year except for £30 in living expenses.

His argument was that the purpose of increased earnings which blessed the lives of hard-working disciples was not to increase their standard of living, but to increase their ability to be generous to those with greater need. He believed that such generosity and sharing of resources (as evidenced in the Acts 2 church) could eliminate poverty if other Christians lived in this manner.

- How hard would it be to live like this, retaining just enough resources for basic needs and giving the rest away?
- Do you know of anyone who lives by this philosophy?

Wesley also believed in a holistic ministry that went beyond making a donation to fight poverty. He believed that disciples also were called to be "friends with the poor," to give of themselves in service and relationship, as well as sharing their material resources. It was a kind of hands-on activism that he saw as an integrated approach to sharing the gospel: doing maximum good, sharing the bounty of God's blessings and preaching the Gospel through a compassionate connection.

- What are some ways that Wesley might modernize his approach if he was alive today?
- How might we use Wesley's example to develop criteria for our own stewardship and generosity goals?

Where Do I Go from Here?

It is my hope and prayer that you have found this introduction to foundational Christian practices helpful, but, as the name suggests, these are designed to provide a foundation. That implies that there is going to be something built on the foundation.

The Christian life is a journey. John Wesley, the founder of the Methodist movement, asks a question that is used today in the ordination process of all United Methodist clergy: "Are you going on to perfection?" Of course all ordinands respond in the affirmative even though they know they have a long way to go. For anyone who might respond in the negative, the question must become "Where are you going?" I think this is an appropriate question for all disciples, not just those seeking ordination to serve as clergy in the church.

The perfection Wesley is talking about is not an absolute perfection. Jesus was the only one who has lived into this level of perfection.

Perfection is about becoming perfect (complete) in our love for God, our love for one another, and our love for the world that God has "so loved" (John 3:16).

The Apostle Paul uses the language of completeness:

> *"I thank my God every time I remember you. In all my prayers for all of you, I always pray with joy because of your partnership in the gospel from the first day until now, being confident of this, that he who began a good work in you will carry it on to completion until the day of Christ Jesus" (Philippians 1:3-6).*

So, how do we continue to move toward this 'completion'?

Find a Partner

It has often been said, paraphrasing John Wesley, that there is no such thing as a 'solitary' Christian. While many might push back against this, pointing to some of the desert fathers who lived in solitude, the point is well taken. It is easier (and lots more fun!) to make the journey together. There are many ways to do this. For example:

- Many congregations offer a variety of small group opportunities for study and fellowship.
- Some congregations offer the services of a discipleship coach or a spiritual director to partner with you in the journey.
- You might consider making the journey with a friend. Spiritual friendship is a great way to practice sharing and holding one another accountable.

Develop a Plan

Throughout this workbook you have been encouraged to identify next steps. These might serve as the beginning of a plan for your journey as a disciple.

Any plan that helps you go somewhere has to be clear about where you want to go and what you want to accomplish. Otherwise, as the Cheshire Cat tells Alice (in *Alice in Wonderland*):

"Would you tell me, please, which way I ought to go from here?"

"That depends a good deal on where you want to get to," said the Cat.

"I don't much care where—" said Alice.

"Then it doesn't matter which way you go," said the Cat. "—so long as I get somewhere," Alice added as an explanation.

"Oh, you're sure to do that," said the Cat, "if you only walk long enough."[1]

One way to help set a direction or to be clear about a vision for your future would be to review the introductory section of this workbook where the six dimensions of the Christian life are described:

A life of Worship

A life of Hospitality

A life of Opening to Jesus

A life of Obeying Jesus

A life of Service

A life of Generosity

For each of these dimensions, a description of maturity in that area was provided. As you ponder these descriptions, consider what God is calling you to be. Then begin to build a plan to get there. Be sure to include in your plan:

What you are hoping for (goals)

Steps to reach those goals

Resources that would be helpful

People who could support you in the process

Learn new spiritual disciplines

Too often the word 'discipline' has a negative connotation. It is seen as something that punishes or restricts.

Nothing could be further from the truth when we are talking about spiritual disciplines. In the Wesleyan tradition, spiritual disciplines are often referred to as the 'means of grace.' Grace is the experience of God's unmerited love. There is nothing we can do to earn grace, and by definition it is not something we deserve.

Spiritual disciplines as means of grace are simply ways (tools, methods, activities, etc.) for placing us in the path of God's grace. They are intentional actions that open us to the love of God being poured into our lives.

These *Foundations* materials have been a basic introduction to foundational Christian practices. But there is so much more!

Consider the following listing:

Meditation	Solitude
Prayer	Celebration
Bible Study	Confession
Fasting	Guidance
Witnessing	Worship
Service	Silence
Simplicity	Sabbath
Stewardship	Submission

There are lots more, but this gives you an idea of what you would like to work with as you continue your journey.

There are a wide variety of great resources to help you explore the spiritual disciplines. Here are a couple of classics to get you started:

Celebration of Discipline, by Richard Foster[2]

Sacred Rhythms, by Ruth Haley Barton[3]

Discover your gifts/Explore ways to serve

There is nothing more rewarding than finding a way to serve that matches the way God has 'wired' you. The reverse is also true. There is nothing more frustrating than trying to serve in an area that does not match your gifts.

If your congregation offers a study group around the process of discovering your gifts, this would be a helpful starting point. For example, many congregations offer a class on SHAPE[4] or PLACE[5] to assist disciples in discovering their giftedness.

If not, building on the work done in this *Foundations* study, I suggest that you review several service opportunities and then pick a couple that seem to be a good match. Try them on for size. If it doesn't seem to 'fit,' try something else.

Discover the freedom of giving

The reality is that we are blessed by being a blessing to others. This is especially true in the realm of our financial resources. However, it is equally true that a majority of people live at the very edge of their financial resources and some even beyond.

The starting point for discovering the freedom of giving is to be in a place where we have the resources available to respond to what God is calling us to do. A great way to reach this point is to participate in a study of biblical principles for financial management. If your congregation offers such a class, (e.g. Financial Peace University,[6] Crown Ministry,[7] etc.) take advantage of the opportunity. It has the potential to free you from the burden of debt and free you to be a generous disciple.

The movement toward generosity begins with proportional giving. I suggest that you pick a percentage of your income to give for God's work and be faithful to that for a year. The next year, consider increasing the percentage by a point or two. Repeat this pattern until you are tithing or beyond.

It is a great feeling to make a difference through our giving!

Growing My Faith by Sharing My Faith

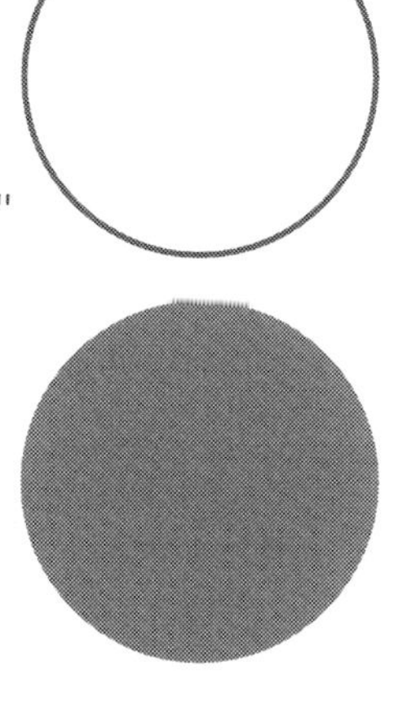

You yourselves are our letter, written on our hearts, known and read by everyone. You show that you are a letter from Christ, the result of our ministry, written not with ink but with the Spirit of the living God, not on tablets of stone but on tablets of human hearts.
2 Corinthians 3:2-3

Jesus says, "Therefore go and make disciples of all nations (people groups)...."
Matthew 28.19

Sharing is a natural thing...

About 30 years ago Becky and I discovered a Tex-Mex restaurant in Ft. Lauderdale, Florida, that was the best Mexican—and maybe food in general—that we had ever eaten: From the fresh salsa to the Tacos al Carbon and the 'fried' ice cream, it was all scrumptious! We began to talk about our great 'find' to family and friends and even church members in the natural course of conversations. Over the years I have had family members and friends and even people who have talked with family members and friends contact me about where to find that great 'Tex-Mex' restaurant. (By the way, we still go there to eat when in the area!) I estimate that somewhere around 25 people have been introduced to this restaurant through our sharing something we enjoy.

The reality in life is that this type of sharing is natural. Sometimes it is about a restaurant, sometimes a great movie, and sometimes about our favorite fishing spot.

What is something you have been excited about and shared with others? Jot down an example or two in the space below:

I think the same is true for our lives as disciples of Jesus Christ. As we experience the love of God flowing into our lives, as we discover the power to engage our world differently and to love others more deeply, it is simply a natural thing to share with others about what God is doing in our lives. In "Christian-ese" (churchy language) we call this our personal witness.

God's Idea

This personal witness idea is actually God's idea. God is a 'sending God.' Throughout the biblical story, God sent many to share the story of what God was doing in our midst. For example:

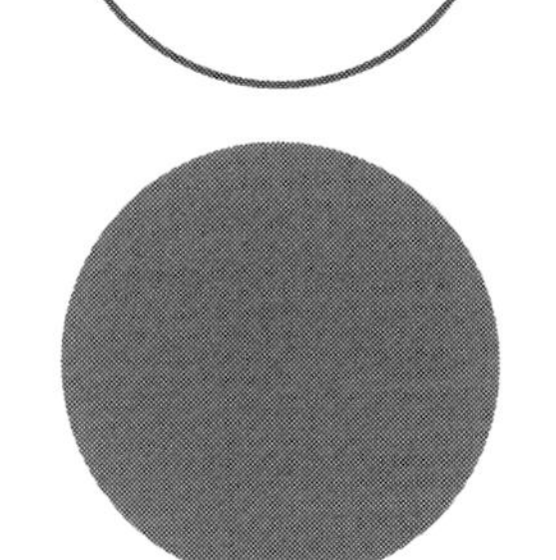

- God sent Abram (later called Abraham) to be a witness in a faraway land and to be a blessing to the nations.
- God sent Moses to share what God had done in his life and to share what God was going to do in freeing the people of Israel from captivity.
- God sent a continuous succession of prophets to share their story of how God was at work.
- God sent His Son, Jesus, to proclaim the Good News of God's Kingdom on earth.
- Jesus sent the Apostles to witness to God's Kingdom around the world.
- Jesus sends us to share what God is doing in our lives. Consider the following:

"As the Father has sent me, I am sending you."

John 20:21b

"Therefore go and make disciples of all nations, baptizing them in the name of the Father and of the Son and of the Holy Spirit, and teaching them to obey everything I have commanded you..."

Matthew 28:19-20

Of course the problem is that this listing can be very intimidating. Not many of us consider ourselves the next Abram or Moses in God's narrative. That may be why so many of us find it difficult to "go…make disciples."

But it's really just something God has wired us to do naturally. We don't have to be great theologians, great leaders, or even great disciples. We don't have to have it all together and know all of the answers. We just have to be who we are and willing to do what comes so naturally. We just have to share our own stories.

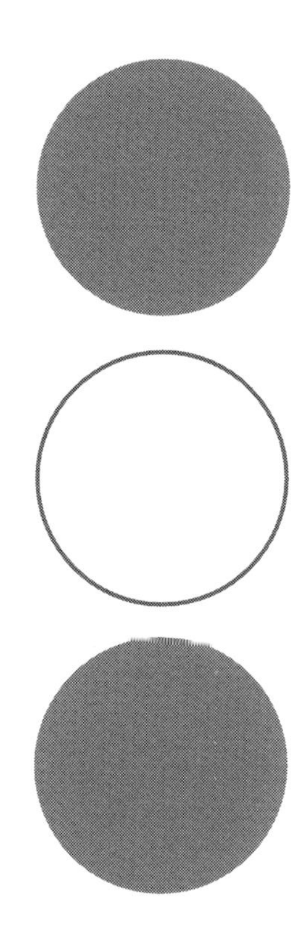

Relationships—Not Programs

There are a lot of programs and techniques used by congregations of all brands. But there is nothing more effective than being who you are in relationship with someone and sharing about what God is doing in your life. In the lingo of a popular ministry of spiritual formation and leadership:

Make a friend.

Be a friend.

Bring a friend to Christ.[1]

Statistically, over the past couple of decades, it has been shown that somewhere between 60-80% of those who come to our churches for the first time come because someone invited them. That's huge! Now, we all know that bringing someone to church is not necessarily the same thing as bringing them to Christ. But it may be a strong support for you in accomplishing the end goal. Let's be clear—the end goal is not to get more people in our pews or chairs for worship. The end goal is to help people discover the amazing love God has for them and the difference a relationship with Jesus could make in their lives.

There are, of course, two sides to this benefit.

As you share your experiences with someone, introducing them to the love of God through Jesus Christ, these experiences continue to be alive in and for you! You become clearer about the ways in which God has worked in your life and you develop an awareness of how God is continuing to work.

While there are many resources to help you consider your faith story and explore how you might share it with someone else, it really is as simple as the title of Bill Hybel's book, *Just Walk Across the Room.*

Of course, it does help to have thought through what you might share. So, use the space below to identify 3-5 bullet points that are key to your experience of how God is working in your life:

With whom might you share your story?

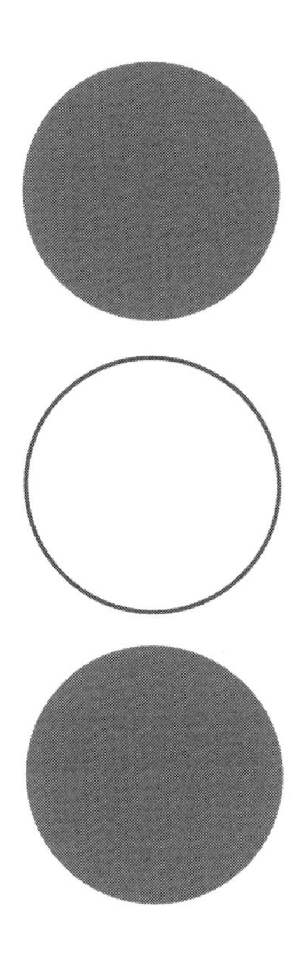

There really are no boundaries to the 'who' question other than it really is helpful if you have a relationship with the person. So you might consider starting with your family, or friends, or co-workers, or those you play ball with, etc.

Some will be interested in your story and others will brush you off! Don't be offended. It is really about what God is doing or going to do. You are simply a vessel for sharing the message.

While there are no boundaries, there are some life circumstances during which people seem to be more open to hearing the Gospel message and being invited to join you at church.

From the life transitions perspective, consider the following:

- Marriage
- Birth of a child
- New job
- Promotion

From a life crisis perspective, consider the following:

- Death of a family member or friend
- Loss of a job
- Divorce
- Moving to a new geographic area
- Health issues
- Aging
- Addictions
- Emotional distress
- Parenting issues
- Care of aging parents
- Loneliness
- Loss of purpose in life
- Lack of self-control

Whom do you know that might be experiencing one of these times of transition or crisis?

Faith Sharing as a Dimension of Christian Discipleship

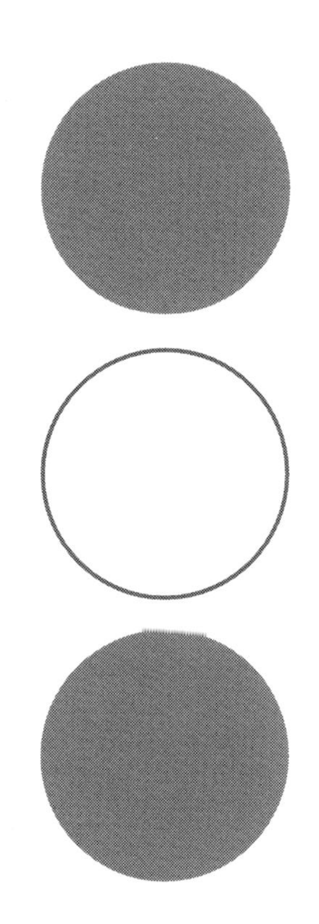

Francis Chan does a humorous video segment during which he contrasts the game of Simon Says with the calling of Jesus Says. Of course, in Simon Says we all try to do what Simon says, but when Jesus says something we talk about it rather than do it. For example, when Jesus says, "Go…make disciples."

He jokes about telling his daughter Rachael to go clean her room:

"She doesn't come back in an hour and say, 'Dad, I memorized what you said. You said, Rach, go clean your room. I can say it in Greek!'

She doesn't get together a study group of her friends to explore what it would look like if she cleaned her room.

She cleans her room.

Yet, when Jesus tells us to go make disciples it's a whole different thing." [2]

While introducing people to God's love is part of our calling, it is also one of our greatest privileges! There is little that brings greater joy to our lives than helping a friend or acquaintance discover a relationship with Jesus.

Faith sharing is part of our journey as disciples. When we start the journey the focus is, of course, on our own relationship with Jesus. As we continue to grow we begin to discover opportunities to share how God is working in our lives with our families, friends, co-workers, and neighbors. But as we move toward maturity, we discover that we are being called to intentionally develop relationships with the unchurched in order to be Christ in their lives and help them discover a relationship with Jesus.

So, how do we get started?

A key to sharing our faith is—intentionality. This actually has two parts:

- Be intentional about maintaining relationships with those outside the church. Too often disciples get drawn into a more restrictive set of relationships that are centered around those who are also believers. Keep your unchurched friends.
- Be intentional about making friends with the unchurched and seeking opportunities to be a witness in their lives.

Consider the following approach which many churches find effective:

- Identify 3-5 persons who do not have a relationship with Jesus (you might consider the life transitions/crises presented previously). Write these names down on index cards or post-it notes.
- Commit to pray for these persons, grow your relationship with them, and look for the opportunity to share your faith with them.

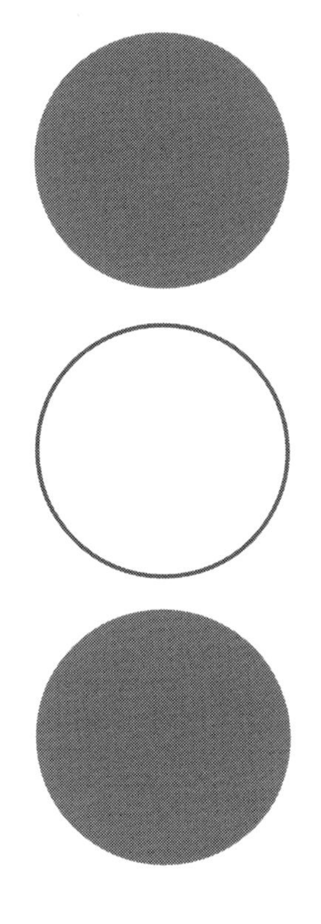

- Place the cards or Post-it notes on your bathroom mirror or some other prominent place where you will be reminded regularly about your commitment.
- Be intentional about praying for these persons and growing your relationship.
- Look for opportunities to invite them to discover the abundant/eternal life you have discovered in Jesus.

Another great way to get started is to "*love your neighbor*" (Mark 12:31).

It is an interesting reality in today's culture that a relatively small percentage of people actually know their neighbors. By that I mean our physical neighbors—the ones who live right around us. A great way to build relationships and be Jesus in people's lives is to start right in our own neighborhood.

For example:

- You might host a monthly (or at least at regular intervals) gathering at your home for a cookout, game night, dinner 4/8 (4 couples), etc.
- Be the 'welcome wagon' for your neighborhood and welcome newcomers by helping them get moved in or providing a meal on move-in day.
- Be available to help a neighbor with some kind of project that takes more hands than they have available.
- Provide childcare for your neighbors to give them an occasional date night.

Suggested Resources:

Just Walk Across the Room, Bill Hybels

Contagious Christian, Bill Hybels

Catch: Attracting and Connecting Visitors (Go Fish), Adam Hamilton

Faith-Sharing: Dynamic Christian Witnessing, George E. Morris

Growing UP: How to Be a Disciple Who Makes Disciples, Robby Gallaty

As disciples move toward maturity in their relationship with Jesus and specifically in their practice of hospitality, the focus of life moves increasingly from a focus on themselves and toward the building relationships with those who do not know the love of God, to be Christ in their lives. In the diagram below some steps toward maturity are identified:

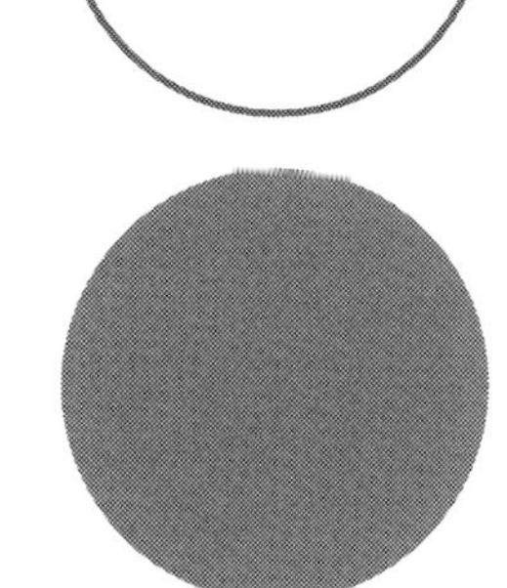

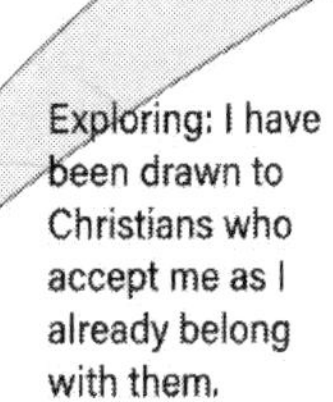

The practice (area) that I want to focus on developing is:

____

Someone who could support me in developing this is:

____

Resources that might be helpful:

____

1 Action Step:

When:

2 Action Step:

When:

The person who will partner with me:______________________________

My prayer is that you will continue to find ways to build upon the Foundation that you have begun to build through participation in this study.

Blessings to you.

Notes

Welcome!

1. Phil Maynard, *Shift: Helping Congregations Back Into the Game of Effective Ministry,* EMC3 Coaching, Florida, 2013, p. 74.
2. Ibid., p. 75.

Building Christian Relationships as Disciples

1. David Kinnaman & Gabe Lyons, *UnChristian,* Baker Books, Grand Rapids, Michigan, 2007, p. 28.
2. Noel Piper, "An Appetizer for the Feast," Tabletalk Magazine, July 1, 2011, http://www.ligonier.org/learn/articles/appetizer-feast/

Building My Relationship With God Through Prayer

1. Brother Roger of Taizé, "Bible and Faith," Taizé, http://www.taize.fr/en_rubrique43.html
2. S. D. (Samuel Dickey) Gordon, *Quiet Talks on Prayer,* Fleming H. Revell Company, 1904, p. 7.
3. Fred Hartley, Everything by Prayer: Armin Gesswein's *Keys to Spirit-Filled Living,* Christian Publications, January 2003, p. 137.
4. Ibid., p. 123.
5. Armin R. Gesswein, *Plead the Promises of God,* http://www.leaderu.com/orgs/bpf/pathways/plead.html
6. S. D. (Samuel Dickey) Gordon, *Quiet Talks on Prayer,* Fleming H. Revell Company, 1904, p. 83.
7. Lawrence Christopher, *The Tickle Fingers: Five Finger Prayer Book,* MF Unlimited, Atlanta, Georgia, 2007.
8. Brother Roger of Taizé, "Letter of 2005, *A Future of Peace,*" Taizé, http://taize.fr/en_article1510.html

Building My Relationship with Christ through the Word of God

1. William Gladstone (1809-1898), British statesman, served as Prime Minister four times
2. Barbara Brown Taylor, *The Preaching Life,* Rowman & Littlefield Publishers, Inc., Lanham, Maryland, 1993, pp. 10 and 55.
3. Wayne Cordeiro, *Devotions and Journaling,* http://www.enewhope.org/nextsteps/journaling

Building a Life of Devotion Through Worship Experiences

1. Ted Loder, *Guerillas of Grace:* Prayers for the Battle, "Let Something Essential Happen to Me," Augsburg Books, Minneapolis, Minnesota, 1981, p. 93.
2. Kathleen Norris, *The Cloister Walk,* Riverhead Books, New York, 1996, p. 32.
3. Wayne Cordeiro, *Devotions and Journaling,* http://www.enewhope.org/nextsteps/journaling
4. Ken Gire, *The Reflective Life,* Chariot Victor Publishing, September 1988, p. 88.
5. Dan Wakefield, *Returning,* as excerpted from *Searching for Your Soul: Writers of Many Faiths Share Their Personal Stories of Spiritual Discovery,* edited by Katherine Kurs, Schocken Books, August 24, 1999.

Building a Life of Service Through the Use of My Gifts and Talents

1. The United Methodist Church website (http://www.umc.org/, Our People, "Exploring Your Spiritual Gifts," "Online Gifts Assessment," "Spiritual Gifts Assessment," http://www.umc.org/site/c.lwL4KnN1LtH/ b.8347315/k.53A8/ Exploring_Your_Spiritual_Gifts.htm (All descriptions of gifts and spiritual gift clusters given in this section come from this website. (Accessed December 31, 2013.)
2. Erik Rees, *S.H.A.P.E.*, Zondervan, Grand Rapids, Michigan, 2006, pp. 37-95.
   Building a Life of Generosity Through Stewardship

Building a Life of Generosity Through Stewardship

1. Richard Foster, *Celebration of Discipline: The Path to Spiritual Growth*, 20th Anniversary Edition, Harper Collins, 1978/1998, p. 84-85.
2. Channel 4, "After Years of Decline, Cash Withdrawals are Again on the Up," May 21, 2012. http://channel4.com/info/press/news/after-years-of-decline-cash-withdrawals-are-again-on-the-up, May 21, 2012.
3. Adam Hamilton, *Enough*, Abingdon Press, Nashville, Tennessee, 2009.

Where Do I Go from Here?

1. Charles Lutwidge Dodgson, writing as Lewis Carroll, *Alice in Wonderland*, Maplewood Books, 1865/2013.
2. Richard Foster, *Celebration of Discipline: The Path to Spiritual Growth*, 20th Anniversary Edition, Harper Collins, 1978/1998.
3. Ruth Haley Barton, Sacred Rhythms: *Arranging Our Lives for Spiritual Transformation*, InterVarsity Press, Downer's Grove, Illinois, 2006.
4. Eric Rees, *S.H.A.P.E.*, Zondervan, Grand Rapids, Michigan, 2006.
5. PLACE Ministries, www.placeministries.org
6. Dave Ramsey, *Financial Peace University*, www.daveramsey.com/fpu
7. Crown Financial Ministries, *Journey to True Financial Freedom Seminar*, www.crown.org

Growing My Faith by Sharing My Faith

1. *Walk to Emmaus, The Upper Room*, General Board of Discipleship, www.upperroom.org/emmaus
2. Francis Chan, presentation at *Verge Conference* and *Mike Huckaby Show*, available as YouTube video titled "How Not to Make Disciples," February 10, 2012.

Made in the USA
Columbia, SC
02 September 2020